THE REA

Emily Thorne considered herself the steady, quiet one of her family; getting on with her job, saving for the future, hardly giving a thought to love and marriage. But was it true, or was she simply unawakened? Perhaps her stormy relationship with the wealthy Demis Kaladonis would provide the answer . . .

THE REALMS OF GOLD

BY

ELIZABETH HUNTER

MILLS & BOON LIMITED
17–19 FOLEY STREET
LONDON W1A 1DR

First published 1976
This edition 1977

© Elizabeth Hunter 1976

For
NANNIE
(Miss Eleanor Wannell)

ISBN 0 263 72341 0

Made and printed in Great Britain by
Richard Clay (The Chaucer Press), Ltd., Bungay, Suffolk

CHAPTER ONE

EMILY THORNE caught the train by the skin of her teeth. She threw her single suitcase and a number of well-filled plastic bags ahead of her and pulled herself rather breathlessly up into the crowded corridor just as the train began to pull away from the station. Bending to retrieve her possessions, she sighed, noticing that she had somehow managed to ladder her tights in the rush.

'You should not be in such a hurry,' a deep, masculine voice said somewhere above her head. There was a faintly foreign inflection to his speech which was attractive without being incomprehensible. She looked up quickly and was annoyed with herself for the momentary curiosity she felt about him. He seemed enormous, standing over her, his clothes immaculate and obviously expensive. She stood up, balancing her plastic bags on her fingers.

'One always has more than one can carry at Christmas time,' she said. 'You know, goodies for the family—that sort of thing.'

He took a selection of the bags from her and peered inside them. 'Ah, it is food! It looks good.'

'It is good.'

His serious expression made her want to laugh. His skin, she noticed, had a golden look as if he spent most of his life in the sun, and his hair was black and curly. He had a strong, unsmiling face that held a ruthless look. On the whole she was glad that he was only a passing stranger.

'You are confident of your abilities as a cook, but you are a poor traveller,' he said firmly. 'You had better sit on my seat and take these packages on your knee. They will soon be crushed out here in the corridor.'

Of course he would have a seat! She followed him meekly to his chosen compartment and found it was a corner seat facing the engine on which he had placed his briefcase, apparently the only luggage he had with him.

'But I can't deprive you——' she began in half-hearted protest.

'Sit down,' he commanded. 'I shall go to the buffet and see if there is a bar where I can have a drink. Will you be all right here by yourself?'

Emily nodded. All right? She was in clover, for she had expected to have to stand the whole way. She was, however, feeling a bit mean in allowing him to search the train for what, she was almost sure, would turn out to be a non-existent drink. She even made a move to stop him, but she was too late and he had already gone, forcing his passage through the crowded train with the ease of an experienced rugby player. He was not, she realised, so unusually tall as she had thought, but he would never be easily over-looked. She expelled her breath with a rush, still feeling the impact of his personality. How her sister would have loved playing heroine to his hero, she thought with amusement. Married or not, she dearly loved to make her mark with every attractive man she came across.

Emily settled more comfortably in her seat and allowed herself to imagine the way her sister would have related the incident to her assembled family. Oh, she would have blown it up into an encounter of major proportions, with herself escaping being kidnapped by a hair's breath, and they would all more or less believe her, for Margaret attracted romance as other, lesser beings dreamed their more ordinary dreams. Emily's brother Patrick was not behind the door either when it came to attracting the opposite sex. It was only herself, the youngest of the trio, whose prosaic approach to life safeguarded her from falling from one exciting romantic adventure to another.

So what was wrong with her? she wondered. Nothing, her common sense retorted. It was only that she liked to be comfortable and high romance was apt to outrage her sense of humour at all the wrong moments. Byronic young men, like the stranger on the train, had no taste for being laughed at, especially when they were intent on using some girl as the perfect foil for their own good looks. Emily, who had watched both her brother and sister choosing their friends among the opposite sex for that very reason since early adolescence, had been less than enthusiastic when her own turn had come to be courted and made much of for no better reason than that she was a Thorne and every bit as pretty as her more adventurous sister.

Her sister had stayed at home until she had married: Emily had gone to London, determined to earn her own living. She had always been the outsider in her family, holding herself aloof from the

7

passionate quarrels and reconciliations in which they all indulged, all that was except her father, with whom she had struck up a quiet, unexacting relationship early in life. Together they had watched the excesses of their loved ones, shrugging their shoulders at the latest display of fireworks from one or other of them with an amused tolerance that went unnoticed by the rest.

'You shouldn't laugh at your mother,' her father had reproved her once when she had been about eight years old.

'She doesn't mind,' Emily had answered. 'She likes to have an audience when she gets excited. The others don't listen to her. Do you?' she had added curiously.

'Always,' he had affirmed. 'I'm her most devoted audience.' And they had laughed together, just as though Emily had been the parent and her mother the child.

And Emily had gone on listening, marvelling at her brother's and her sister's capacity for falling in and out of love, and offering appreciative exclamations in all the right places whenever the story of the latest conquest was being recounted.

'You should try falling in love yourself!' Margaret had remonstrated with her when Emily had been struggling to get her elder sister into her wedding dress. 'Let yourself go, Emily! You have the whole of London waiting for you, but you never seem to go anywhere interesting—or meet anyone nice!'

'I manage,' Emily had said with a smile.

'But do you?' her sister had insisted. 'Why do we never hear about any of your young men? Aren't you ever asked out at all?'

'Fairly often,' Emily had answered with wry humour. 'I'm particularly in demand for parties, though I sometimes wonder if my canapés don't add to my allure more than my fatal charm.'

'I daresay,' Margaret had agreed without hesitation. 'You know, you're every bit as good-looking as Patrick and I are, but there's something lacking. I can't imagine you having to fight off half a dozen goodnight kisses after a dance——'

'Well, if I did, I wouldn't tell you about it,' Emily had cut her off, her grey-green eyes alight with laughter. 'I'd be too busy nursing my bruises after knocking all their heads together!'

'I suppose you have been kissed?' Margaret had asked frankly.

Emily had laughed out loud. 'Once or twice. I am a Thorne, after all,' she had answered, and had refused to take up Margaret's open invitation to tell her all about it.

'Well?' her sister had demanded.

Emily had opened her eyes wide. 'Well what?' she had returned.

Emily leaned back and closed her eyes. It would all be the same this Christmas, she supposed. She wondered if her brother-in-law would be there. When last heard from, her sister had tearfully wept over the telephone that she never wanted to see him again. Emily had listened as always, but the ache in her shoulder-blades had transmitted itself to her voice when she had suggested that Margaret should try for once to see somebody else's point of view. Margaret had been first hurt and then angry.

'You're jealous!' she had declared. 'You've always

9

been jealous of me! Patrick has always said so, but I never believed him until now!'

Emily pursed her lips together. She had never envied her sister's greater charm and she wouldn't have said thank you for her spouse, whom at first meeting she had dismissed as petulant and at the second as far too weak to hold one of the volatile Thornes for long. She didn't even like him very much——

She opened her eyes and saw that the stranger was back, a can of beer in his hand. He had his back to her, standing before the window, his feet slightly apart to facilitate his balance, but she could see his profile every time he poured the liquid down his throat. His nose was too heavy for his face and the muscles of his jaw were too uncompromising for Emily to suppose that he would be an easy individual to deal with. She had had enough of strong-minded individualists in her own family, she decided. When it came to her turn to marry she would choose someone cuddly and kind and very, very undemanding!

He turned his head and saw her looking at him. Far from smiling at her, his mouth tightened.

'Are you all right?' he asked her.

She was startled. 'Of course. Don't I look all right?'

He shrugged, his eyes deliberately examining her hands. 'You are unwed,' he observed. The jolting of the train made him stand nearer to her than she liked and she carefully moved her knees well away from his leg that was nearest to her. 'But perhaps you are promised?' he added, his eyes straying over her with a languid, insolent interest.

Emily's eyes sparked dangerously. 'Do I have to

have some man to be all right?'

His eyes met hers. 'I think so,' he said.

'Then you can keep your thoughts to yourself!' Emily retorted. 'I'm much better off as I am, heart-whole and fancy free.'

He raised his eyebrows with a small shake of the head. 'Your protest is too pat for me to believe that it comes from the heart,' he dismissed her angry comment. 'It is good you are going home to your family. No doubt they will see you have suitable partners at the Christmas parties and you will find yourself married to one of them before you know it. It must be a worry to them when you are on your own in London—or do you live with some other relations there?'

'No.' Emily tore her eyes away from him. This was the most ridiculous conversation and she had every intention of bringing it to a swift close. 'You're not English, are you?' she remarked sweetly. 'In Britain women live their own lives nowadays. We prefer it that way.'

'Some may, but in Britain too there are still some girls feminine enough to feel incomplete without a man to look after them. You are not the only one.'

That was a cue for laughter if there had ever been one, but Emily was too angry to be amused by his arrogance. 'I'm well able to look after myself!'

Slowly he shook his head at her again. 'Would you say the same if you had missed the train? Or if I had not given you my seat to sit on? Is that why you became a good cook——?'

Emily struggled to her feet, her face furiously angry. 'Have your seat!' she almost shouted at him.

11

'I can manage very well without it! And even better without your personal remarks!' she added for good measure. 'Go on, sit down in your precious seat and I hope you enjoy it!' She gave him a push and became angrier still when she found that she couldn't shift him. 'I want to go outside, if you'll move out of the way.'

'Why are you so angry with me?' he asked, as calm as she was vexed. 'Do you always lose your temper so quickly and so thoroughly?' For the first time his mouth relaxed into a faint smile. 'Too quickly, *korítsi*. Sit down again and relax. I shall leave you in peace until we arrive at your station. You will need help getting out with all your packages, no?'

She subsided back into the seat, wondering what could be wrong with her that she couldn't dismiss his outrageous comments with the lightness they deserved. Why get all hot and bothered about nothing at all? she demanded of herself. A few personal remarks from a foreigner wouldn't hurt her. She had read often enough that they dealt in them all the time, so he was probably being no more than polite in his own way.

She forced a reluctant smile. 'For the moment I forgot you are a foreigner,' she told him by way of apology. 'In England we usually talk about the weather to strangers, not how they manage or mismanage their lives.'

'In Greece we are a little more direct,' he acknowledged. 'But you are right to be cautious, after all.' He made an expressive movement with his hand. 'You are afraid all these people will look the other way if I should act improperly towards you?'

Put like that she was forced to acknowledge her fears to be ridiculous, but she couldn't help thinking that if he wanted to he would find his way round any difficulty. Thank goodness he couldn't really want to!

It was a relief when he retreated into the corridor and, after a few moments, disappeared down the train, probably in search of another beer. Ashamed that she should be such a coward, Emily rose quickly to her feet, gathered her possessions about her and began to push her way through the crowds in the opposite direction. If Patrick were to see her in the company of such a man there would be no end to the questions she would be asked over the holiday. They would go on and on at her, asking her all about him and when she was going to see him again, and she would be as vulnerable as she always was to their teasing, half wishing that she could take the wind out of their sails by announcing, 'He's Greek, and rich, and he won't take no for an answer, so I'm marrying him next week!'

A man fell against her in the corridor, ruining her *brioche aux pécanes*, and into the bargain she nearly dropped the bag that held the Christmas puddings.

'Sorry, love,' the man said, not caring at all.

'I expect I'll survive,' she answered wearily.

He gave her a doubtful grin. 'You're not angry, are you? No one has any right to be angry at Christmas time.'

'I'm never angry!' she retorted. He was the second person to accuse her of being bad-tempered and she couldn't understand it. What had happened to her usual aloof placidity in the face of all disasters? Gone with the Greek stranger! Though why he should have

13

had that effect on her she found it impossible to guess.

The man's grin grew more confident. 'Getting out at the next station, are you? Want a hand with those things?'

Emily thanked him gratefully, glad that she was nearly home. Only a few more minutes and then she would be driving away in Patrick's comfortable car to the house where she had been born and brought up.

Not many people got out at the next station. Emily thought she would have known if the Greek had been among their number, and she heaved a great sigh of relief that she had managed to free herself from his attentions. That there was also no sign of Patrick did not immediately occur to her. She exchanged a few words with the ticket collector, as she always did, and found a clear space in which to put down her packages and wait.

It was not Patrick who came running up the slope to the station, however, but Margaret. Emily watched her sister's eyes focus on her and the startled step backwards of surprise.

'Was the train early?' Margaret demanded.

'Two minutes late,' Emily returned.

'Oh well, you didn't mind, did you? I'm here now. It's good to see you, old thing. The whole household is in chaos because they didn't expect me on my own, but they did expect Patrick, and there were even rumours that you were bringing someone from London with you. What's he like? I don't mind telling you that Pat and I were beginning to worry about you. It's not *normal* to be as reticent as you are about your affairs! Where is he, by the way?'

'Where is who?' Realising that Margaret was not

14

going to help her with the plastic bags or her suitcase, Emily began stringing them on to her fingers, lifting them carefully so that no further harm could come to their contents.

'*Him!* The man you've brought with you.'

'Oh, him! I left him behind in London,' Emily said airily. What man was she supposed to be bringing with her? 'Did mother tell you about him?'

'Of course she did. Father is as close as you are.' Tears came flooding into Margaret's eyes. 'He's not well. Oh, Emily, we had such a scene last night, too, when I told them that I was leaving Peter. You know what Father is, marriage is for life and all that stuff. That's why it's so important you should take his mind off me by producing this man. How could you leave him in London?'

'Well,' Emily said, 'as I don't know who he is it never occurred to me to do anything but leave him there.'

'Emily! Don't be maddening! Mother must have got the idea from somewhere! And don't you care that I'm leaving Peter?'

'Of course. Tell me all about it,' Emily invited, mentally making a note to expect Peter some time on Christmas Eve for the Grand Reconciliation that would inevitably take place.

Margaret made the most of her story while Emily stowed her luggage away in the boot of the family car. 'Nobody was glad to see me,' she ended tragically. 'Father said I should be making our own Christmas for Peter, not running around without him, and Mother only wanted to know where Patrick was and why he wasn't coming home. Then she came up with this story about you and Father looked *pleased*! He said at least one of us was behaving in a responsible manner and that it was right and proper that you should bring him home to meet the family—which was a hit at me because I didn't let anyone see Peter until I was absolutely sure of him. You know what Mother is with young men, and I wanted him looking at me and not at her.'

'She should have told me,' Emily said. 'I expect I could have found somebody who would have been glad of a family Christmas.'

'Could you have done?' Margaret looked at her with narrowed eyes. 'You do have boy-friends, then?'

'It depends how you define the term,' Emily answered. 'I know quite a number of men, if that's what you mean, but I don't regard any of them as my exclusive property.'

'You're not in love with any of them?'

'Not really,' Emily said. 'They're just ordinary men.'

'Most of us fall in love with ordinary men!' Margaret exclaimed crossly. 'What's special about you?'

'Nothing,' Emily admitted. 'But there's nothing special about them either.'

'Well, you'd better think up somebody special before you see Father!'

Emily got into the front passenger seat with a disdainful shrug. 'I'm not sure——' she began.

'The whole family is relying on you!'

Emily didn't say anything. She would wait until she had seen her father by herself, she thought.

'What's wrong with Father?' she asked.

'Been working too hard. Mother's on at him to sell

16

the business, or to take a partner, but he won't, of course, unless he can find exactly the right person. Only he has to do something because the travelling is getting too much for him. There's some chance of a merger with another firm that's also in the import/export business, but I don't think they specialise in the eastern end of the Mediterranean as Father does.'

'Does Father want to retire?' Emily asked.

Margaret nodded. 'He said so last night. I suppose he's getting old.'

Not very old, Emily decided mentally. She wished she knew more about what he did, or that Patrick had joined him in the firm as her father had always wanted, or even that Peter had shown a spark of interest in the business world. Should she herself have accepted his offer to train her to take over from him? But the business world had never been hers. She had always wanted to teach Home Economics until she could save enough to open her own restaurant, perhaps in her own home town, and she had done well at it—very well. It wouldn't be long now before she could think about resigning from her present post and starting out for herself.

'If he retires,' she said aloud, 'he could take an interest in my restaurant. I can't imagine him doing nothing.'

But Margaret refused to take her seriously. 'Surely you're not still on about that old chestnut? You'd do far better to find yourself a husband who would help Father instead of expecting him to help you! It's funny that you should be a Thorne, Emily. You're not at all like the rest of us. You've always been the selfish one.'

17

Emily raised her eyebrows. 'Have I?'

'You've always gone your own way and taken no notice of the rest of us! Well, this time it's your turn to do something! Father needs cheering up and you're the only one who can do it!'

'I'll see,' Emily compromised.

She had time before they drew up outside their parents' house to open her handbag and run a comb through her dark hair. She reapplied her lipstick, staring at herself in the tiny mirror of her flapjack as though she had never seen herself before. Was she selfish? Perhaps she always had been. It was certain that she *looked* a Thorne, having the same black hair and the same grey-green eyes as her brother and sister, but she had always been quieter than they, her movements more gentle and her interests more serious. Did that mean she was selfish? She gave a little shake to her head, refusing to consider the matter further.

Margaret stopped the car outside the front door. She put an anxious hand on the sleeve of Emily's coat.

'Please do something!' she begged. 'It's not a lot to ask of you. Couldn't you pretend to be fond of someone for a while, just to make the old boy perk up and take interest again? Surely you owe us that?'

Emily could not honestly remember either Patrick or Margaret ever having done anything for their father, but she had not been home much recently and perhaps circumstances had changed. She suddenly wanted to see her father very badly for herself. She would know the minute she saw him if things were serious or whether her sister was exaggerating as

18

usual. She had to know!

Mrs Thorne greeted her youngest child with absent-minded affection. 'It's too bad of Patrick not to be here over the holiday to help entertain your young man,' she murmured. 'He'll feel lost, poor boy, with so many women all round him and your father having to rest all the time. What are we going to do with him?'

'Emily says she hasn't got a young man,' Margaret announced from the doorway.

'Not?' Mrs Thorne looked concerned and grief-stricken. 'Have you quarrelled with him too?' she demanded of Emily. 'Well, you'll just have to make it up again if you have. Peter and Margaret are quite quarrelsome enough for one family. Bicker, bicker, bicker, all the time!'

'Not any more,' Margaret assured her cheerfully. 'I told you, Mother, we've broken up.'

'So you may have. He'll be here for his portion of turkey all the same,' her mother retorted with unusual insight. 'But what are we going to do about Emily?'

Emily laid her plastic bags down on the kitchen table, rescuing the more fragile edibles from their travelling containers.

'Do you have to do anything about me? Father will understand. He knows how you all embroider on real life——'

'*Emily!*'

'We do not!'

'No?' Emily transferred a crumb of *brioche* from its bag to her mouth. If they ate it for tea that afternoon it wouldn't be too bad. 'Someone must have

19

thought up this mythical boy-friend of mine.'

'*You* did!' her mother claimed firmly. 'He rang up here last week and asked to speak to you—and if you didn't give him this telephone number, who did? I can't remember his name now, but it had a foreign sound. He sounded enchanting!'

'But I've never heard of him!' Emily felt winded and she sat down hastily on the nearest chair. 'He rang up *here* and asked for *me*?'

Her mother nodded. 'Miss Thorne——'

'That might have been Margaret,' Emily protested.

'Not for nearly a year!' Margaret triumphed. 'Besides, he knew all about you.'

'He can't, if I don't know anything about him. Mother, you must have got it all wrong. He can't have asked for me!'

'Ask your father, dear. He was in the room when I took the call. He may even remember the poor man's name. Go and ask him, Emily dear, and stop fiddling with those cakes and things. I've been meaning to have a word with you about that for some time now. You're too old to think about nothing but food. Still, never mind, this man will be a nice new interest for you.'

'Yes, Mother.'

Mrs Thorne managed a brave smile. 'I'm glad you're here, child. I've done my best to nurse your father back to better health, but I've never felt at my best in the sickroom. Why don't you go and see him now and find out if he feels well enough to come down for tea?'

Emily needed no second invitation. She ran lightly up the stairs to her father's room, tapping her finger-

20

nails against the painted door.

'What have you been doing to yourself?' she asked him as she crossed the room in answer to his brief command to come in.

'Didn't they tell you? I collapsed in the office and had to be brought home in an ambulance. Now I'm busy resting and getting on your mother's nerves! There's nothing for you to worry about, Emily. I can cope.'

Their eyes met. 'Sure?' Emily insisted softly.

'Quite sure. I felt better the instant I heard you were thinking of getting married soon. He rang up here, did your mother tell you?'

Emily nodded, feeling cold in her middle. 'I'm not sure——'

Her father looked up at her, smiling. 'Is *he*?'

Emily conjured up a vision of the Greek stranger on the train. 'He's always sure—about everything!' she said in an aggrieved voice. 'Sometimes I don't like him at all!'

'But he means to have you?'

'I don't know. I think so.' Her tongue felt several sizes too large for her mouth. 'I'm not banking on anything yet.'

'No?' It was obvious her father didn't believe a word of that. 'What is he like?'

'He has a golden look,' she said abruptly. 'He never smiles and he thinks women were made for men to order about. He has black, curly hair and very light eyes. He isn't handsome—his nose is too big for his face, but one can't forget what he looks like. He has a little scar on his jawbone——'

'My word, you have looked at him, haven't you?

Your mother said something about him being a foreigner?'

Emily hesitated, then nodded. 'He's Greek. Very Greek!'

Her father's interest was caught. He looked at his daughter with a decidedly speculative air. 'And what does he do, this Greek of yours?' He waited for Emily to answer, apparently unaware of the panic that had laid its icy hand on her thoughts. 'Are you very much in love with him?' he asked more gently.

'*I don't know!*'

Her father patted her hand consolingly. 'If he hadn't telephoned here you wouldn't have told us a word about him, would you, my dear? Don't shut us out of your life altogether, Emily. I'm your father just as much as I'm Patrick's and Margaret's—more, I sometimes think, especially when I'm tired and have to accept help from all and sundry as I do at the moment.'

'I'm not trying to shut you out. I really don't know.'

'But you do know his name?'

His name! He hadn't *got* a name! At least none that she knew!

'His name?' she repeated. 'Of course I know his name. He's called—his name is——' She shut her eyes and tried to think of any Greek name she knew and, surprisingly, one came floating to the surface of her mind—a name that was undoubtedly Greek and not in the least famous. 'His name is Demis Kaladonis,' she said.

22

CHAPTER TWO

'THERE! I told you so!' Margaret declared in triumph. 'Father looks oodles better already. He can't wait to meet this fiancé of yours.'

'He's *not* my fiancé! Nor will he ever be! I told you, I didn't actually lie about it—at least, not at first. I just went along with the conclusion everybody had jumped to. How can I be engaged to a figment of my own imagination?'

'He's becoming more real by the moment,' Margaret observed. 'He has a name now, and a nationality. I'm beginning to think that you do know such a person but, for some reason best known to yourself, didn't want us to know about him.'

'Oh, Margaret, really! I told you——'

'Well, who knows what you get up to in London all by yourself! He doesn't sound made up. Figments of the imagination don't have little scars on the jawbone.'

'That was someone I met on the train,' Emily admitted, knowing it was unwise to mention the Greek stranger but somehow quite unable to stop herself.

Margaret's eyes widened. 'On the train? What happened? Did he try to pick you up? The Greeks are devastating lovers, so I'm told!'

'He saw I had a lot of parcels and allowed me to sit in his seat,' Emily said primly. 'An ordinary, commonplace event that I'd rather you didn't blow up into being the grand passion of the century.'

'But, darling——'

'I mean it!' Emily flared up. 'I don't like playing silly games, and you've managed to ruin my Christmas completely for me already. I hate pretending to Father at the best of times——'

'It's for his own good.'

'I wonder. I think he would have preferred the truth had he been consulted. What have we given him? A few false hopes that can never be realised! There's no such person as Demis Kaladonis, so how is he going to be Father's favourite son-in-law and inherit the business from him? Tell me that!'

Margaret refused to be depressed by any such realistic talk. 'I don't believe he doesn't exist,' she said grandly. 'If you ask me, you're a dark horse, Emily Thorne, and you do know such a person! How did you think up the name on the spur of the moment like that? Answer, you didn't! You know a Demis Kaladonis very well, only you don't want us to know about him because you've always been so superior about our love affairs that you don't want us to witness the fall of the ice maiden in case we laugh at you! Well, it hasn't come off, because I'm laughing now!'

If Margaret believed that, she would soon convert her mother and Patrick to her way of thinking, Emily realised with increasing desperation, and she would never hear the end of it. It was her own fault too. She should have refused to diverge from the narrow path of truth right at the beginning, selfish or not. *Demis Kaladonis*! She was beginning to hate the very name of the man she had invented. Nor was she enjoying the guilty feeling she had every time she looked at the

24

worn, drawn face of her father and saw the new contented, satisfied glow that had come to him.

He had been busy all afternoon. At intervals Emily
had heard the telephone bell sound as it does when
the receiver is replaced, and she had wondered what
business he had been able to do two days before
Christmas.

'Don't do too much,' she had begged him when she
had taken him up his tea. 'We want you downstairs
for Christmas, and you won't be if you don't rest
now.'

'I'll be there.' Her father had grinned happily to
himself. 'As soon as Peter arrives I'll come downstairs.'

'Margaret says he isn't coming,' Emily had reminded him.

Mr Thorne had dismissed that with the contempt it
deserved. 'Of course he's coming. The young fool will
learn in time that Margaret exaggerates everything,
just like her mother, and that the only way to handle
her is to pay no attention to the verbal excesses that
she likes to indulge in.' He had turned and looked up
at Emily. 'Now you, my dear, would do better if you
let down your back hair more often. Still, I can't
imagine Demis Kaladonis allowing you to bottle
things up for long, however. Is that what frightens
you about him?'

'Who said I was afraid?'

'Aren't you? The Greeks like to be the masters in
their own homes, and you've always valued your independence to the point of obstinacy. No one expects
a woman to make it all by herself—not even in these
days. Oh well, it's too late for you to allow me to help

25

you with your restaurant now. It won't be any use to you in Greece.'

Emily had stood her ground with a courage she had not known she possessed. 'You don't understand!' she had suddenly cried out. 'I'm not going to marry anyone! You're all making far too much of a—a chance acquaintanceship with no one in particular!'

But her father had only laughed. 'Demis Kaladonis will never be nobody in particular!' he had told her.

He had been right, too, in thinking that Peter would join them that evening. Emily had thought her brother-in-law would have left Margaret to stew in her own juice until late on Christmas Eve, but he arrived just as they were sitting down to eat the meal she had prepared with all her usual flair.

'Thank God for something fit to eat!' he murmured as he sat down beside his sulky-faced wife. 'I'd have come a long way for that if nothing else.'

'Then you should have married Emily and not me,' Margaret shot back at him.

'Sometimes I wish I had!'

Emily looked down at her plate, wishing she could like him a little more than she did. Why did he have to be stupid enough to stroke Margaret's fur the wrong way just for the fun of it? It had always embarrassed her to have to watch their quarrels, and she was shrewd enough to know that they both knew it too, and that it added a zest to their sparring that would not have been there otherwise.

'Have you much last-minute shopping to do tomorrow?' she asked him, hoping to turn the conversation. Peter was famous for his last-minute Christmas bargains.

He turned to her, his eyes hard and unsmiling above his grinning mouth. 'Absolutely not, sister fair! I'm to be your father's messenger boy for the day, it seems. I can think of better ways of spending Christmas Eve, but'—he shrugged his shoulders—'if one marries into a family like yours, one has to take the rough with the smooth.'

'Meaning?' Margaret asked him dangerously.

'I have to run round after you and pick up the pieces you've carelessly left lying around—and not only you but your family too!'

Mrs Thorne uttered a wail of dismay. 'Peter! You're not talking about me, are you?'

'Not this time, Mother dear.'

Emily tried to cut him out of her thoughts. Her mother had apparently not noticed the barbed tone with which he had addressed her, but she had. She always did. He scarcely ever spoke to any of them without that underlying sneer in his voice.

'Then who——?' Mrs Thorne asked, puzzled.

'It's Emily who has mislaid her property on this occasion,' he said.

That startled them all. 'Nonsense!' said Emily. 'I even remembered your favourite mince-pies after the complaints that there weren't enough for you last year.'

'Oh, leave him alone!' Margaret drawled. 'It's me he's getting at. It always is.'

Peter looked at Emily and laughed. 'So innocent and so deceitful!' he whispered to her. 'And I always thought you were different from the rest of your family. Tell me, what's he got that I haven't? Or do you hand him the frozen mitt whenever you meet

27

too? What's special about him?'

Emily heaved a sigh. She had thought better of her father than that he would tell Peter about her supposed affair.

'If you're talking about Demis,' she said, knowing that he would be unable to follow her into this particular flight of fancy, 'he's the son of Apollo and the beautiful Coronis. His skin is the colour of gold and he doesn't feel the cold. On the contrary, the very stones come to life and warmth if they are lucky enough to feel his feet upon them.'

Peter's look told her that he hated her, but it was her mother who burst into delighted laughter. 'Oh *yes*! I remember *him*! Your father told me about him on our honeymoon. He was brought up by some mythical beast and learned his powers of healing from him, and he was punished by Zeus for raising too many of the dead and disturbing the balance of nature. Now, whatever was his name?'

'Demis Kaladonis, I presume,' Margaret put in.

'Don't be so literal, darling,' Mrs Thorne reproved her. 'I must say I'm looking forward to meeting this young man if he's all you say he is, Emily. I simply can't understand how you came to meet him?'

Emily flushed, and Margaret supplied, 'On a train!'

'Hasn't he got a winged chariot of his own to travel in?' Peter said with sarcasm. 'What a comedown for a Greek god!'

'They're more dangerous when they're pretending to behave like other men,' Mrs Thorne observed. 'Now that you have met him, Emily, you'd better marry him as quickly as possible before——'

'Oh, Mother, really!'

28

'It's well known,' her mother insisted, 'that the Greeks, be they gods or men, have no morals when it comes to the opposite sex. But don't worry, my dear, this one has me to deal with and I certainly shan't allow him to leave you in the lurch!'

Emily could only stare at her open-mouthed. Was it possible that she had already forgotten that Demis Kaladonis was as much her invention as he was Emily's own? It was she who had made him a foreigner and had said he had telephoned the house asking for Miss Thorne. Surely not even her romantic-minded mother could have convinced herself that it had actually happened and that this fictional being had a real existence.

This thought came back to worry her during the night. They all seemed to believe in Demis Kaladonis! There had even been a moment when she wished she could believe in him too, but wishes didn't turn dreams into real men. And, in a way, that aspect of the situation concerned her most of all, for she had never indulged in idle dreams. Indeed, she could imagine few more uncomfortable experiences than being swept off her feet by the kind of person she had made out Demis Kaladonis to be.

By morning she had herself firmly under control and was able to ignore Peter's barbed comments and the rest of her family's fantastic flights of fancy with all her usual indulgence. As always when she was home, they left the cooking to her, her mother with a sigh of relief, and her sister with a long speech about how she had to sort out things with Peter as Emily would doubtless understand and was therefore going out with him for the rest of the morning.

'Will you be back for lunch?' Emily asked.

'Probably,' Margaret answered. 'Unless something better turns up. It doesn't matter, does it?'

Emily thought of the meal she was preparing and sighed. 'No, do as you like. If you're not here, Mother and I can make do with something else and we can have the pie for supper.'

'Great,' said Margaret. 'I knew you wouldn't care. See you later!'

Emily enjoyed making pastry. She could make better pastry than anyone else she knew and she invariably felt a glow of achievement when she placed her pies in the oven to cook, knowing they would come out exactly the right shade of golden brown and delectable to the taste.

She had just reached the stage of adding the water when the front door bell rang. She waited a moment to see if anyone else was going to answer it, but when it rang again, she wiped her hands on her apron and went out into the hall to answer it herself.

She opened the door wide, a smile of welcome on her face that died into a look of astonishment as she saw who was on the doorstep. She tried to shut the door quickly, catching her breath, but she was too slow to prevent him from putting a foot inside the hall.

'Go away!'

He pushed the door open and came inside as though she were no more than a rag doll to be brushed out of his way. Emily hid her face against the door and clung to the latch as though her life depended on it.

'*Please* go away!' she begged.

He stood, looking at her for a long moment, then he put one hand over hers and firmly shut the door, before dropping his hand onto her shoulder and turning her round to face him.

'Miss Thorne?'

'Why won't you go away?'

'Why should you want me to? I have been to some trouble to come here, so why should I now go away?'

There was no answering that. 'How do you know my name?' she asked instead.

'Did you expect me to forget it so soon?'

'But we didn't exchange names on the train,' she objected. The warmth of his hand on her shoulder made her conscious of how close he was and she took a hasty step backwards, catching the skirt of her dress on the corner of the hall table. 'Did we?' she added more uncertainly. He must have found out her name from somewhere.

'I do not remember doing so. It was not then that I learned your name.'

'Then when——?'

The golden glow to his skin was very noticeable against the dark panelling of the hall. 'I have always known it,' he said with a touch of arrogance that somehow forbade her to inquire further into the mystery. 'But on this occasion I have come to see your father,' he added.

'He's been ill,' she told him. 'I'm afraid he's not getting up until this evening. Couldn't you wait until after Christmas?'

'After Christmas I am going home to Greece. You don't have to be so unwelcoming, Miss Thorne. He knows I am coming.'

'He didn't say anything to me about it.'

'No? Does he always discuss his business affairs with you?'

She took the implied rebuke badly. 'Someone has to see he's not bothered with commercial travellers and people like that on Christmas Eve!'

His eyebrows rose. 'If it will put your mind at ease, I will tell you that your father asked to see me himself. His son-in-law telephoned to me this morning telling me to come at once. Now, will you please take me to him?'

She stood up very straight, not enjoying being put in the wrong so easily and with such finality. 'What name shall I say?' she asked stiffly.

A flash of amusement crossed his face. 'Demis Kaladonis,' he said.

Emily was quite sure she was going to faint. There was a terrible stillness in the hall and the blood drained away from her face, leaving her looking like a frightened ghost.

'Did you say Demis Kaladonis?' she breathed, hanging onto her senses with everything she had.

He held up his briefcase in front of her and she read the name in both Greek and Roman lettering on its side. It was the last straw! She must have seen it on the train, which was why it had come so easily to mind when her father had asked her the name of the man she was in love with.

'But you don't exist!' she exclaimed. 'I mean, of course, you do exist, but your name can't be Demis Kaladonis! You'll have to change it while you're talking to my father. Can't you have another name for an hour or two?'

He looked astonished, which didn't really surprise her. 'Miss Thorne, do you feel quite well?' he asked her.

'No! Oh, *please* couldn't you be called something else? My father need never know——'

'But he would know, Miss Thorne. This is not the first time I have met your father. We have done business together before.'

'Oh no, it can't be true!' Emily groaned. 'You'll have to go, Mr Kaladonis! I'll never be able to look my father in the face again as it is! Go back to Greece, please do, until I'm safely back in London! By that time I may have been able to think of something——'

'Do I really need explaining away?'

This was worse than anything. Emily stared at him in silence, crushing her hands together in acute misery. What would he think of her when he discovered the use she had made of his name? A strong hand covered both of hers and she winced away from him as if his flesh burned her.

'You'll never believe it!' she gasped.

'Try me,' he invited her.

But she couldn't find the words to tell him anything. And then, when she realised she would have to say something, anything, to keep him away from her father, her mother came floating into the hall, for some reason best known to herself in a long evening dress, and exclaimed with delight,

'Mr Kaladonis! How lovely to see you at last. I've heard so much about you. Don't let Emily keep you in the hall, dear boy. My husband is waiting to see you, and I want to meet you properly too. Emily has never brought many boys home, and now that she has a real live fiancé it seems too good to be true!'

'It is too good to be true,' Emily said in a voice of doom. 'Mother, I keep telling you——'

'That it isn't official yet. Yes, I know, darling, you don't have to tell me again. But you wouldn't have said anything at all if you hadn't been sure in your own mind that Demis—I may call you Demis, mayn't I?—is the right man for you! You'd better take him upstairs to your father before he thinks you don't mean to introduce him to your family after all.'

Emily blinked. 'Mother, what are you doing in that dress?'

Her mother executed a neat dance step round the hall, spreading her skirts around her. 'Do you like it? I thought I might wear it tomorrow. What do you think? You'll be coming too, won't you, Demis?'

'Thank you, *kyría*. It will be my pleasure.'

'No, it won't be!' Emily burst out. 'You *must* have made other arrangements for Christmas!'

'No, no,' he assured her blandly. 'I changed my plans immediately I heard from your father, besides'—he gave her a droll look—'*thá efharistithó polí na sás ksanathó.*'

'I speak a little Greek,' she warned him.

'Then you know what I said?'

She shook her head, anxious now to follow the strict line of truth even though it was now too late to do her any good. 'Not exactly,' she said.

'I said I should be pleased to see you again,' he told her. 'It is never dull when you are about,' he added with an edge to his voice.

'It will get worse! For your own sake, you'd do

much better to go away now!'

'Emily!' Her mother sounded completely scandalised. 'You must learn to share your loved ones with a better grace,' she reproved her. 'Your family has a right to be interested in what you do. Take Demis up to your father at once, dear, and try not to make out that we're all ogres waiting to pounce on him.'

Obediently, Emily began to mount the stairs. The nightmare was closing in round her, and it should have been some comfort to know that nothing worse would ever happen to her than what was happening now.

'What are you seeing my father about?' she demanded abruptly as she gained the landing.

Demis Kaladonis' eyes glittered dangerously in the shadows behind her. 'That is my affair,' he answered. 'But you can answer a question for me. Why don't you share your life with your family, *thespinis*?'

'I do! What there is to share——'

'A woman should not be too independent, I think. Not in her emotions at least.'

'My emotions are my own business!' she snapped.

'One day they will be your husband's business. Have you thought of that?'

No, but she thought he was the most impertinent man she had ever met. She would have told him so too, if she hadn't been aware that she had been a great deal more than impertinent as far as he was concerned. And there was her father to be considered also. She opened her eyes very wide.

'*Kýrie*, my father thinks—they all think—would you mind very much not denying anything until after Christmas? You can say what you like to me, but my father is recovering from a heart attack and he may have a setback if he knew—I don't know how it happened, and I'm most frightfully sorry, but there's nothing to be done about it now, is there?'

'I will answer that after I have seen your father,' he said quite gently. 'He and I understand one another very well. You may safely leave him in my hands.'

She summoned up all the courage she had left, looking him straight in the eyes. 'You know, don't you?'

'I think so,' he admitted.

'It wasn't as you think! I didn't mean——'

He permitted himself a faint smile. 'In Greece we know better than to leave it to young girls to arrange these things for themselves,' he told her. 'They will always make everything into a big drama if one allows them to do so. Such matters are better left in the hands of men, *né*?'

'*Me? I* make a big drama?' She gasped with sheer, burning indignation. 'I don't dramatise things!' she denied hotly. 'I leave that sort of thing to my mother, and Patrick, and Margaret. I'm the quiet one of the family!'

He raised a brow, considering her dispassionately. 'You think so? I think you are destined to be the Thorne in some man's flesh, more so than either your brother or your sister. You are the most demanding of the three, are you not?'

'Certainly not!'

'Is it necessary that you should shout so that the whole house can hear what we are saying?' he asked, affably enough. 'To hear raised voices is more likely to disturb your father than anything I may say to him.

36

Afterwards, I shall take you out in my car and you can shout all you like——'

'I *never* shout!'

He raised his eyes heavenwards and took a step towards her. Quite what she thought he was going to do, she didn't know, but a shaft of fear went through her and she turned with a rush towards her father's bedroom door, wrenching it open and practically flinging herself inside in answer to Mr Thorne's gruff command to come in.

'Father, may I present the Kyrios Kaladonis? *Kýrie*, this is my father.'

Her father took in her raised colour and he exchanged glances with the younger man. 'Come and sit down, Demis. I hope Peter explained to you why I have to receive you in my bedroom and not downstairs? It was good of you to come so quickly.'

'I was glad to do so.' Mr Kaladonis remained standing by the door, holding it open for Emily to make her exit before sitting down.

She determined to put off the moment. 'Father, shall I bring up some coffee or—or something stronger?'

'No, dear. I have some *ouzo* over there on the table and I'm sure Demis won't mind pouring it out. You'd best leave us to talk.'

'But——' she objected.

Demis Kaladonis put a peremptory hand on her arm. 'Do as you are told, *thespinis*. Your father and I have things to say to one another. *Parakaló piyene!*'

'Yes, leave us, Emily,' her father added in English, amused by her obvious irritation.

'*Grigora!*' Mr Kaladonis insisted. 'Go quickly!'

He shut the door firmly behind her and she rubbed her arm where he had held her, sure that he must have hurt her and annoyed to discover that he hadn't. It was nonetheless outrageous that he should handle her in such a way. Worse still was the way he had looked at her, as though he had the right to study the intimate details of her shape, almost as if he owned her! He had done just the same on the train, she remembered, making her acutely conscious of some unnamed need in herself that she would have preferred to have known nothing about. If she had had the courage she would have looked back at him in the same way and seen how he liked it! Only he already knew all there was to know about his manhood and nothing could undermine his masculine confidence in himself, whereas she—she had seldom thought of herself as a woman before all else, needing to respond to the initiative of some man before she could fully come alive.

The door opened behind her and she scuttled down the stairs, her heart beating at twice its normal rate in case he should discover her still on the landing and jump to the conclusion that she had been trying to overhear what the two men had been saying to each other.

The unmade pastry in the kitchen came as a surprise to her. She had completely forgotten that she had been in the middle of getting the lunch when the doorbell had rung. Automatically, she finished making the pie and put it in the oven, washed her hands at the sink and pulled off her apron, all the time trying to think of some plausible explanation she could give the man when he finally came downstairs.

'What a lovely man!' Her mother's voice brought her back to what she was doing. '*Very* Greek!'

Emily shivered. 'I wish I hadn't told him I understood some Greek,' she said. 'He can be so much nastier in his own language!'

Her mother laughed, a soft, knowing laugh that made Emily feel thoroughly uncomfortable. 'You're behaving very badly, Emily dear, but I expect he knows you well enough to realise that you don't mean half of what you say.'

'He doesn't know me at all!' Emily sat down on the nearest chair, her eyes kindling as she saw her mother's bland expression. 'We invented him between us—and now look what's happened!'

'Including his name and the scar on his jaw?'

'At least you might admit that he never phoned to me here,' Emily went on. 'You could tell the truth about that!'

'But he did ask for you, dear. He wanted to speak to Miss Thorne. He was quite clear about it.'

'I don't believe you,' Emily said flatly.

A shadow crossed her feet and she looked up quickly to see Demis Kaladonis standing over her. She jumped visibly. The stricken look on her face reflected her inner feelings. Yet he didn't look angry.

'You may believe her, *korítsi*,' he said from a great way off. 'I did telephone you here. Put your coat on, Emily, and I'll take you out to lunch. We can talk after we have eaten, *né*?'

She felt as though she would never want to eat again, but she nodded her head and went to fetch her coat, allowing him to slip it up over her arms and

39

even to turn her round to face him and do up the buttons for her.

'Did Father tell you——? Is he all right?' she asked awkwardly.

'Quite all right. We came to a very amicable agreement, so you have no need to worry any more. Are you ready?'

She nodded again. Not worry! That would be the day! 'Mr Kaladonis——'

He put a finger across her lips. 'Hush! Say it in Greek,' he commanded her.

But she didn't know the words to ask him if he was angry. *'Entáksi,'* she murmured instead, signifying that she was ready to go and that everything was in order.

'Good girl,' he commended her, and she went out with him without a backward look.

CHAPTER THREE

THE car was large and comfortable. Emily noticed the name of the hire company on the key-ring and saw it was a London firm. So he didn't always travel by train, she reflected, but perhaps he had wanted to use it over the Christmas period when the trains didn't run.

'I don't know how I'm going to begin to explain——'

'Then don't,' Mr Kaladonis advised.

She was tempted to take his advice, but in justice she didn't see how she could. He was owed some kind of explanation even at the expense of her self-respect —and she would make it, just as soon as she could find the right words to make it clear how she had got herself—and therefore him—into this pickle.

'You have every right to be angry,' she admitted, increasingly concerned because he seemed to be taking the whole episode in his stride just as though it were an ordinary occurrence that was hardly worth his bothering about. 'Do you dislike driving on the left-hand side of the road?' she added, seeing him hesitate as they came to the end of the drive.

'Not really,' he answered. He cast her a fleeting look that was nonetheless comprehensive. 'Relax, *korítsi*. I am not an ogre waiting to pounce on you!'

'No,' she agreed, feeling slightly breathless and turning her face away. 'Was it awful with my father?'

41

'Why should it have been? He is a very nice man with a good grasp of what his business entails. We came to an agreement almost immediately.'

'Oh.' Hadn't they discussed her at all? 'Are you in the same kind of business?'

'My interests are many and varied, but your father's firm fits in very nicely with some aspects of my own. It would be useful to me to have a well-established outlet in this country for some of my products. But I doubt if you would be interested in all that.'

'Why not?' she retorted.

'I understood that none of his children were much concerned with how he made his money—not even his son. Am I wrong about this?'

'I suppose not,' she said. 'Patrick has always wanted to do something creative and my father could well afford to indulge him in that. Margaret is married now——'

'And before she married?'

'It wasn't worth her while working,' Emily excused her sister. 'You ought to understand that, being Greek.'

'Many Greek girls work nowadays, even if there is no necessity for them to do so. You work for your own living, don't you? Why are you different from your sister?'

'I lecture in Home Economics, but that's only a stepping-stone to what I really want to do, which is to have a restaurant of my own. I have great plans for that!'

'Tell me about them,' he suggested.

She looked at him uncertainly. 'Are you interested,

or being polite?' she asked him.

'I am always interested in any new business venture,' he assured her.

Emily was surprised. Somehow she had never thought of her projected restaurant as being a business. To her it had always been the prize at the end of the hard slog she had set herself, first qualifying in her chosen subject and then teaching it to others, saving frantically while the balance in her bank grew steadily until the day she could realise her dream and put her cherished ideas into practise.

'It should always be an occasion to eat out, but how many restaurants remember that? Most of them are too routine in their approach. They forget the little touches of glamour that can make or break a party for their customers.'

'And you would not?'

'I hope not.' She struggled against the temptation to tell him one of her most dearly held theories, and lost. 'Catering is a vocation,' she informed him. 'It has to be a privilege and a pleasure to feed people well, or it's nothing. One might as well pound a typewriter, or stay at home being a social success like Margaret —not that I have anything against that sort of thing, but I want the meals I serve to be an event in people's lives!'

'Have you thought what place your husband will take in these plans?' he inquired with a sidelong glance that she found more than a little disturbing.

'I shan't marry for ages!' she declared.

'What makes you think that?' he pressed her.

'I've never met anyone I want to marry. Besides, I'm almost sure I want a restaurant of my own more

43

than I want a husband.'

'I'm glad you are only almost sure. You may find yourself marrying sooner than you think.'

She shook her head. 'Never!'

'It is what your father wants for you. You have raised his expectations now that his ambition for you is about to come true. Won't it be a little difficult to disappoint him when he is not well and is so pleased to have everything working out so happily?'

Emily clenched her fists in her lap. 'Did you discuss it with him?' she asked.

'Of course. It was why he wanted to see me.'

'But you said you'd been talking business with him?' Her mind whirled as she contemplated the disaster her deception had set in motion. 'Did you explain that we had never met, except that once on the train yesterday?'

'I thought it better not to mention the extent of our friendship——'

'But we're not friends!'

'No? Perhaps you are right. A man and a woman are seldom friends.'

She sensed that there was a rebuke implicit in his words. 'I didn't mean to involve you in this. Why don't you go away and leave me to get out of the mess on my own? I can explain things to my father——'

'You would soon find yourself in difficulties,' he observed. 'Your father has old-fashioned ideas about the way he wishes the women of his family to behave. Besides, it suits me better to leave things as they are.'

She could scarcely believe her ears. 'How can you?'

'When we have had lunch,' he promised, 'I will tell

you what your father and I have arranged for our mutual future and we will make our plans together. It is not half as bad as you think. All you have to do is leave everything to me. Will you do that?'

'How can I? I got myself into this——'

'Did you? I think your mother and your sister may have had something to do with it. But you need not worry any more. I shall look after you.'

'I don't think you realise how bad it is,' she sighed. 'You wouldn't be so sanguine if you did.'

'No? Perhaps I too planned it this way. Have you thought of that?'

There was something in his tone that warned her he was not joking but was trying to tell her something. She shrugged. 'I don't understand.'

He navigated through the town traffic as though he did it every day, coming to a stop outside the most fashionable restaurant in the place.

'I booked a table here,' he told her. 'I am not sure it will come up to your high standards, but it seemed adequate when I called there earlier.'

'It's the best there is—at the moment,' she conceded. 'One day I hope to open up in competition and then my restaurant will be the best locally!'

He put a hand over hers, preventing her from opening the door of the car. 'I'm afraid not, my dear. Your father and I have made other plans for you. There is no need to look like that. Your father is deeply concerned for your happiness. Do you think he would do anything less than the best he can for you? Well, do you?'

Her mouth felt dry. 'He has no say in my life,' she said at last. 'Oh, I don't mean to sound hard and horrible, but I've earned my freedom. I've earned every penny I spend, and that's the way I like it. My life is my own, and nobody is going to tell me what to do with it!'

'If you were a man that would be admirable,' he said with calm arrogance. 'But a woman must always adapt to the lives of others. You cannot always earn your own money. You will marry and have children, and then it will be for your husband to decide your way of life. Until then your father has that responsibility.'

'Mr Kaladonis, this is the twentieth century, or hadn't you heard?'

His glance mocked her. 'Human nature doesn't change,' he said.

He put out a hand and opened the door for her. For an instant she felt the hardness of his body against hers and she was suddenly afraid of being swept away in his train and that there would be nothing she could do about it, for no one would listen to her and she wouldn't be able to resist him all by herself.

She slipped out of the car and stood on the pavement waiting for him to come round to her. He parked the car with an ease she could only envy and had locked all the doors in a flash, trying them as he moved round to her side, before putting his hand firmly on her elbow and leading her into the restaurant. She pulled her arm free of his grasp and refused to meet his eyes as they were ushered across to their table. But that didn't stop him looking at her. He waited for her to sit down and then threw himself into the chair beside her, his eyes watching her every movement.

'Mr Kaladonis——' she began at last.

'You had better make it Demis,' he drawled.

She flushed, wishing she had never heard either part of his name, or that she had remembered where she had seen it, or anything not to have told her father that he was the man she was in love with.

'Demis, if you wish,' she replied. 'It doesn't matter because after today and, if we have to, tomorrow, we shan't be seeing each other again.' Not if she had anything to do with it!

He went on looking at her. 'How old are you, Miss Emily Thorne?' he asked finally.

'Old enough to be able to run my own affairs!'

'Your father thinks differently. He has never been happy about your living on your own in London. He thinks, as I do, that he should have taken steps to keep you at home where he could keep an eye on you. Big cities are no places for young girls to be on their own. They are bound to fall into trouble sooner or later.'

Emily's temper kindled at his words. 'I never had the least trouble in London,' she denied. 'I never had any trouble at all until I met you!'

His eyebrows rose. 'You were lucky. In Greece it would have been otherwise. Are Englishmen so slow that they will allow such a pretty girl to get away from them?'

'There's never been anything I couldn't handle. At least my compatriots know when to take no for an answer.'

'But, like the rest of your sex, you prefer the spice of a little danger?' he suggested, amused. 'You under-

47

stand our Greek ways better than you will admit. You will not be as lost among us as I had feared.'

She froze. 'I'm not going to Greece!'

His light eyes rested on her indignant face. It was impossible to tell what he was thinking, but she was sure that whatever it was it boded no good for her. She tried to give him back look for look, but failed miserably when she realised that he could not be forced into telling her what had transpired between him and her father before he was good and ready to do so. It simply wasn't possible to bend his will to hers using normal, direct means. In his opinion she was a woman and therefore to be despised, and if she lost her temper with him, it would be no more than he expected from a female of her years. Very well, she thought, she would see what charm could do. She was not a Thorne for nothing!

She smiled slowly. 'I'm glad you weren't embarrassed by my foolishness,' she said aloud. 'Many men would have been.'

'You were embarrassed enough for both of us,' he said dryly. 'It takes a great deal to embarrass me. You would be well advised not to try to do so.'

She shrugged her shoulders. 'Still, it was a terrible thing to do to you and I'm truly sorry about it. I'll put things right with my family as soon as I can.'

'I have already done so. Your father and I are in complete agreement that your future is safe in my hands. It has been a great relief to him to have everything settled to his satisfaction. He has been wanting to retire from his business for a long time now, but neither your brother nor his son-in-law were the right people to take over from him. He knows that I was already interested in buying his firm before I ever met you and that has made it easier still for him to relinquish the reins into my hands. His health depends on his peace of mind, Emily, and I forbid you to disturb him unnecessarily any further. Is it understood?'

She was really angry now. '*You* forbid? Who are you to tell me how to treat my own father?'

'As your future husband I think I have some rights in the matter, don't you?'

'How dare you? I wouldn't marry you if you were the last man left on earth!' She lowered her voice to a whisper, conscious that the half-dozen other people in the restaurant were staring at her. 'I'll never forgive you! Never!'

'But it was you who told your family that you wanted to marry me. I saw no reason to contradict you, that's all. Would you have preferred me to have denied any knowledge of your existence to your father?'

'No,' she admitted. 'At least not at once. But you didn't have to agree to marry me, did you?'

'Not even when you will bring me your father's firm as a going concern as your *proíka*?'

'You mean my father's giving you his whole business if you marry me?'

'He recognises that a Greek seldom takes a woman empty-handed, even in these days,' Demis acknowledged. 'It's an arrangement that suits us both.'

'Well, it doesn't suit me! I'm not for sale, Demis Kaladonis! My father's business is nothing to do with me——'

'And your father?'

She glowered at him across the table. 'That's unfair,' she said crossly.

He gave her an interested look. 'Perhaps it is. Emily, won't you accept that we have only your best interests at heart? You will enjoy Greece, I promise you that, and your father will have peace of mind. He will receive a generous pension, which your mother will inherit should anything happen to him, and he will have the joy of knowing that the firm he built up has not passed completely out of the family. Will you deny him all that?'

She couldn't believe that he was serious. 'Marriage isn't a business deal,' she said. 'When I marry it will be for love. I couldn't accept being married to someone on any other terms.'

'I see,' he said. 'It is the intimate side that worries you. I had forgotten for the moment that you are English and romantic. In Greece we are more realistic about these things. Marriage is not the ordeal you imagine. I am confident that I can teach my own wife to love me in time. It is something we can work at together, don't you think?'

She was caught up in the brilliant fire in his eyes and, just for a moment, she even thought that she might quite like to marry him. But that was ridiculous! And she would tell him so. It shouldn't be difficult to make it clear to him that she preferred to make her own plans and stick to them. She wanted her own restaurant more than anything else in life, not a shadowy future in exile from her own land because it suited him and her father. It was outrageous that such a possibility should even have been put to her.

'Demis, how can you consider marrying someone you have no feeling for? Is my father's firm so valuable to you?'

He shrugged. 'I have to marry some time.'

'Someone who doesn't want to marry you?'

The glimmer of a smile came into his eyes. 'She would not be reluctant for long.'

'You can't possibly know that!' Emily looked down at her hands and was annoyed to discover that they were shaking. She smoothed down her skirt over her knees, aware only of the pounding of her heart in her chest and the most extraordinary desire to have this golden Greek say that she did mean something to him. But of course he wouldn't. To him, marriage was a business deal, no more than that. Hadn't he already made that clear to her?

'Why can't I know it?' he asked in a coaxing tone. 'I would not have promised your father to make you happy if I had thought it beyond my powers.'

'Oh, how conceited you are!' she exclaimed, but she didn't sound as certain as she would have liked.

'Am I?' He looked surprised by the idea. 'I don't think I am. I am not exactly ignorant of the ways of your sex——'

'No, you wouldn't be!' she said with deep feeling.

'I have two sisters,' he told her, amused. 'I think they would give me a good reference if you were to ask them for one. When my father died they naturally became my responsibility and remained so until the elder married—the younger is so still. My younger brother lives with my elder sister now until he is old enough to start work with me. We are a very close family and you would be very welcome among us.'

'But I wouldn't be your sister!' she said.

'Is that what bothers you?' There was something magnificent about his complete calm, she thought, uncomfortable as she found it. 'It need not,' he went on. 'It is necessary for us to get married first, but you will have all the time you want before you become my wife, *agapí*, I promise you that. It will be like an extended holiday for you—until you yourself want to be my wife.'

'And supposing I don't? Supposing I want to come back to England and live my own life?'

'That too can be arranged. If after two or three years you want to come back to England, I shall not stand in your way. More, I shall set you up in the restaurant you want so badly myself. I have no wish to force you against your will.'

She considered his offer carefully, mulling it over in her mind. 'It costs real money to set up a restaurant,' she warned him. 'And it's much more likely that that's what I shall want to do.'

The fire in his eyes burned high. 'It's a risk I'm prepared to take. Well, Thorne in my flesh, what do you say? Are you going to marry me?'

She took a sip of wine, knowing that she had to refuse him. Her self-respect was at stake, and her cherished independence, because, whatever he might say now, he would expect to control her life as a matter of course if she once gave way to him. He expected it now——

'What if I don't?' She asked the question aloud, but she was really asking it of herself. He might buy out her father anyway, but she doubted if he would trouble himself further with the Thorne affairs. She would go back to London, of course, and go on working towards her goal, but it seemed a lonely existence and one that she couldn't find any appetite for continuing after all. It was what she had always wanted, but thinking about the room where she lived and the College where she taught, it seemed a grey, uninteresting way of life. How could she have changed so drastically in a few minutes? Was the appeal of Greece really so great for her?

'I don't know what to do,' she said. She looked up at him. 'I don't like being taken for granted,' she added.

'Have I done so?' he demanded. 'Come, Emily, admit that you want me to make up your mind for you. Independence is for men; women need to be cherished and protected from the harsher aspects of life. You will be far happier when you have me to turn to. You will have time to blossom into the lovely woman you were meant to be, and you will be glad then that you listened to me.'

'Will I?' Her voice sounded as though it belonged to someone else. 'You don't understand! It was a terrible thing to do, to pretend that I had fallen in love with someone in London. It was worse still to borrow your name and for you to arrive like that. It would be even more improper to marry you for my father's sake, and to allow you to keep me when I shan't be giving back anything to you, for I'm not in the least bit in love with you. How can I agree?'

'But you would like to come to Greece with me?'

She paused. 'I've always wanted to go to Greece,' she said.

He put his hands across the table, grasping her

fingers in his. 'Won't you trust me to look after you, my little Thorne?' he asked her. 'I promise you, you will not regret it.'

She couldn't say anything at all. She tried, but the words caught in the back of her throat. His touch was warm and comforting. He was very strong, but he was gentle too, and the pressure on her fingers was almost a caress. She blinked away the tears that had rushed into her eyes and nodded her head.

'You will marry me?' he insisted.

She nodded her head again. 'I suppose so,' she said.

Strangely, the thing that frightened her most was telling her own family that she had agreed to marry Demis Kaladonis. How would she explain her *volte-face* to them? What would they think of her for meekly agreeing to be the wife of a man she had met only once before, and that fleetingly on the train? They would think her completely mad, and she wasn't at all sure that they wouldn't be right!

But her family did not think her mad.

'You could have confided in your own mother,' Mrs Thorne had complained with ill-concealed triumph at this turn in her daughter's affairs. 'Anyone would think you didn't want to share your happiness with us.'

'She always was selfish!' Margaret had chimed in, managing to sound both sulky and envious in the same breath. 'She's always pretended that she hasn't a romantic bone in her body. It isn't fair!'

Demis had looked very knowing. 'I believe she is the most romantic-minded of you all,' he had said, and Emily was very conscious of his glance. 'Woe

54

betide me if I disappoint her!'

'You won't!' Margaret had assured him, with a discontented look in Peter's direction. 'It's far more likely to be the other way round.'

And he hadn't denied that, Emily had noticed, and she knew then that he thought it too. He had weighed her up and had found her wanting as a woman. If her father's business hadn't been thrown in on her side of the scales, he would never have given her a second look. She ought to welcome the fact that there was no danger of his wanting her as a woman, she thought, but she was now far from sure about this.

She watched her sister flirting with Demis Kaladonis with all her customary ease and wondered what would happen if she, Emily, were to treat him to the same display of fluttering eyelashes and pretty half-pouting movements of the mouth. Would he think her more of a woman then?

'And how is your mother?' Mrs Thorne threw into the general conversation suddenly. 'Emily mentioned her yesterday. Coronis, didn't you say her name is, dear?'

Emily held her breath, feeling a perfect fool. 'I was joking, Mother,' she murmured.

'Coronis? *Coronis!*' Demis stood up and advanced across the room towards her. 'Now what made you think of her and me in the same breath, I wonder?' His eyes, which had a trick of reflecting any light that was going, rested on her briefly. He could well have been the son of Apollo who brought light to men. Hadn't she read somewhere that the Greeks to this very day would greet the new-born day with a kiss for Apollo? And there had been a German archaeologist

55

who had denied Apollo his eminent place among the gods, dismissing him as one who had only lesser powers of no account. Worse still, he had made his statement at Delphi, the god's own shrine, and had lost his way out walking and had been found dead later on, slain by the sun, for he had died of heatstroke. 'Do you think I look like the god of healing?' Demis asked her.

She did her best to make an easy reply. 'Not really. You haven't got a beard. Asklepios always has a beard.'

'You didn't tell us that yesterday,' Margaret pointed out. 'You told us he was the colour of gold and that he always felt warm. Not a very accurate description, since he has black hair and nobody could help being cold on such a freezing day!'

Demis seemed amused. 'Do you know why Asklepios is always warm?' he asked Emily.

She shook her head. 'I only know that Coronis rejected Apollo for the love of a mortal man, only a crow betrayed her to the god, who changed the bird from white to black for his pains. He had his twin sister, Artemis, shoot Coronis with her arrows and afterwards her body was burned, but it was remembered that she was about to give birth to Asklepios and he was rescued from the pyre and given to the Centaur, Chiron, to be brought up by him.'

'But the fire of his birth warms his blood to this very day.' There was a curious ring in his voice. 'Like his father, he has a way with beautiful young women. You had best beware, if you think I am anything like him!'

'It's too late to tell my daughter that,' Mr Thorne

56

said. 'I prefer the tradition that says the god-hero was born in the vicinity of Hieron of Epidaurus, on Mount Myrtion, which has been called Titthion ever since, meaning "the mountain which gave the breast".'

'I prefer it too,' Demis said. 'Perhaps because I, too, was born at Epidaurus.'

The colour drained from Emily's face. 'And what was your mother's name?' she asked.

He looked at her quickly. 'What did you suppose? Her name was Coronis also.'

'And I suppose your father was Apollo too!' Margaret taunted him, bored by all this talk of something she didn't really understand.

Demis smiled easily. 'No, my father's name was Spyros. He is dead now, so, you see, both my parents were mortal.' He turned back to Emily, the smile dying away. He sat down beside her on the sofa, running his arm along the back of it behind her head. It was a peculiarly possessive gesture that she supposed she would have to grow used to. As it was, she was intensely conscious of the golden skin of his hands and face and the aura of masculine warmth that came from his body. He touched her hair with his fingers and she tossed her head away from him.

'What else do you know about the Greek gods?' he asked her.

'That they are dangerous to play around with,' she said coolly, not looking at him.

'Very dangerous if you displease them,' he replied, 'but they can be kind. You will have to walk warily in Greece and make us all love you.'

'It depends who all of you are,' she retorted, a

little frightened by the prospect.

His fingers returned to her hair. 'You had best start with the men and graduate to the gods, *agapí*. There's not a man in Greece who won't think himself a hero if you smile on him!'

It was an impossibly romantic thing to say, and she guessed he only did so because her assembled family expected him to pay her compliments.

'I thought you already were a hero.' She turned the tables on him.

The light in his eyes grew brighter still. His hand fell from her hair to her chin, turning her face towards him. 'To you I mean to be more than a hero, a god!' he said. And he kissed her lightly on the lips.

CHAPTER FOUR

IT was difficult to tell anything about Greece from the airport at Athens. Huge airport buses gobbled up the passengers and disgorged them outside some buildings that were in the process of being rebuilt. From there they were ushered up a flight of stairs to pass through passport control and customs. To Emily nothing seemed quite real, least of all herself.

I shouldn't have done it! I must be mad! she thought to herself. She shuffled along in the queue behind Demis, frozen with fear as to what she might have agreed to in the safety of England. She was not in England now. She was in a strange land, where they spoke a strange language, and where she knew nobody—nobody at all, for least of all did she think she knew Demis Kaladonis!

He had her passport with his own. It was new and shiny, but reassuringly British. He had changed so many things that she had been half afraid he would insist on her changing her nationality too, but surprisingly he had not.

'I like to think I shall have an English wife,' he had said. 'The English and the Greeks have always gone well together.'

She doubted the truth of that herself. Her father had told her many stories of united Greek and British efforts during the war, in which he himself had participated. That had been where he had first learned the Greek language and when he had made the valuable contacts that afterwards had been the basis of the import/export business he had set up. But they had all been men together, and she had grown up knowing that a Greek's attitude to women was very different from the British one. In Greece, women were the servants of their men and they behaved accordingly. The fact that in return they were valued and protected as much because they were women as in their own right seemed very small consolation to Emily at that moment.

She stood to one side while Demis changed some traveller's cheques at the airport bank.

'There is someone over there trying to attract your attention,' she told him when he finally turned away from the counter, stuffing the notes into his wallet.

He looked over where she was pointing and a wide smile broke over his face. It was seldom that he smiled, she thought. If something amused him, his eyes would brighten and she would know that he was laughing deep down inside, but his expression would remain as stern as ever. Not for the first time since that moment when he had put his ring on her finger, she wondered if she weren't secretly afraid of Demis Kaladonis—and if she hadn't been right from the first moment she had set eyes on him on the train taking her home.

'Is she one of your sisters?' she asked him.

'Good heavens, no! That's Hermione. She's an old friend of mine. Come and meet her.'

Emily thought he must be very fond of her to smile at her like that, and she could see why. The other girl was beautiful, with the tawny eyes that some Greeks have and a skin that had been out in the sun too much to be termed delicate, but which a careful use of cosmetics had done much to hide. But she was more than beautiful, she was the most vivacious, outgoing creature that Emily had ever seen.

She could scarcely wait for Demis to get through the barrier before she had flung her arms round his neck and kissed him warmly on the cheek and mouth. A flood of Greek welcomed him home, but was soon cut off by his answer.

'Hermione, this is my wife, Emily.'

The Greek girl looked completely overset. 'Your wife, Demis?' she said in English. 'You are married to this girl?'

'That's right,' Demis said easily.

Emily felt the Greek girl's pain in her own heart. She hadn't given a thought to Demis' previous life in Greece, she realised. Of course there had been many girls in his life, but possibly this one was the only one who had had hopes that he would marry her. It might have been friendship on his side, but it had plainly been considerably more than that on hers.

'Hermione Kaloyeropoulou,' Demis introduced her. 'You'd better call her Hermione as we all do.' He smiled again at the Greek girl, a warm, devastating smile such as Emily had never hoped to receive from him. 'In Greece women seldom use their family names,' he added over his shoulder. 'Most people will call you Emily, or Kyría Emily if they don't know you well.'

'My father is Spyros Kaloyeropoulos,' Hermione put in, her eyes pebble hard. 'Perhaps you've heard of him?'

Emily shook her head. 'I'm sorry——'

'He owns an international airline—among other things,' Hermione drawled. 'Until today he had hopes that Demis was going to go into partnership with him. But'—she shrugged—'now that he has married you, he probably has other plans?'

Emily was shocked by the other girl's frankness. 'We don't pay much heed to a girl's dowry in England,' she said.

'So? What makes you think I was discussing my *proíka*, Kyría Kaladonou? Is that why Demis married you?'

'Probably,' Emily admitted, deciding that whatever she said Hermione was unlikely to believe her.

Demis gave her an impatient look. He didn't relish having his private affairs discussed by mere females, Emily noticed. But what did he want her to say? That she had married him to preserve her father's peace of mind?

'Is it why?' Hermione pressed him, hugging his arm to her in what Emily privately considered was a shameless display, the more especially as she watched her husband take full advantage of the implicit invitation that was being offered to him as he entwined his hand round her waist and caressed her body through the thin material of her dress.

'You should know me better than that,' he answered huskily. 'It was enough to see Emily to know that I had to have her for my own. She is very lovely, *né*?'

Hermione pretended to shiver. 'But too cold for anyone as hot-blooded as you, Demis! Does she respond to you as ardently as a Greek girl would?'

Emily strove to disguise her disgust. That she failed was revealed by her husband's open amusement at the expression on her face.

'You must behave, Hermione. My little English wife is easily embarrassed. She isn't used to these things being talked about openly. Isn't that so, Emily *mou*?'

'I have always been told that Greek women are more demure than we are,' Emily murmured. 'Yet I can't imagine asking a man such a thing in England. At least, I hope I wouldn't.'

Hermione broke into delighted, throaty laughter. 'She has claws, this wife of yours!' she exclaimed. 'And she is not afraid to use them! You must remember, Emily, that Demis and I are very, very old friends. We have seen life together. How should I restrain my tongue with such a person? It would be impossible. We are too much part of one another for that.'

'That was in the past.' Demis actually smiled at her. 'We've both moved on since those days.'

But had he? Looking at the two of them together, Emily doubted it. Not that it mattered to her what lay between them. Or, at least, it shouldn't have done, but it did. It was a matter of hurt pride, she supposed. She might not want Demis for herself, but neither did she want to have his past flaunted so obviously before her. She had, after all, taken his name as his supposed wife, and she found that she didn't like to think of anyone knowing that she was something less than his wife in fact.

'I left the car across the way,' Hermione was saying when Emily came out of her day-dream. 'Your car, that is. I'm going home with somebody else.'

Demis patted her cheek affectionately. 'Anyone I know?'

Hermione pouted. 'If you do, you shouldn't!' she gurgled. 'Your wife will think you're jealous of me if you ask such questions.'

He frowned. 'If he's who I think it is you'd better watch your step, my girl. Your father wouldn't approve.'

'He didn't approve of you either, but that never stopped us! I live my own life, my dear, as you should be the first to know.'

He laughed, shaking his head at her. 'Be careful you don't go too far. Money doesn't buy everything, *korítsi*.'

'So I have learned today, Demis *mou*. I had hoped —but there, we'll always be friends, won't we?'

Emily noted that her husband avoided answering that. Instead he drew her to him, rather as if he had belatedly remembered her presence, and dropped a kiss on the point of her nose. 'We must be going. I want to get to Nauplia tonight if it's possible.'

'Are you going by road?' Hermione asked him. 'It takes much longer.'

'The yacht has gone to Aegina. Giórgios—that's my brother-in-law,' he added for Emily's benefit, 'is worried about some of the pistachio trees. He's overseeing some new spray they're trying out on them. Barbara has gone with him—to keep him company, or so she says.'

'Will you leave your wife behind when you go on your travels?'

Emily felt Demis' eyes on her face and met the

suddenly fierce look in their depths as confidently as she could, head on, lifting her chin in a gesture of defiance.

'There is no time when a man doesn't want his woman by his side when she is loving,' he said inscrutably. 'I am no different from any other husband in wanting that.'

She looked at him quickly, wondering what he meant. Would a Greek woman have given herself without love? Emily didn't know. She bit her lip. What was the matter with her? She had been straight with him right from the beginning. He knew that she would never have married him at all if he had wanted her to be his wife in fact.

In her confusion she somehow missed Hermione's departure. Demis waved to the porter who had gathered up their luggage, and guided her out into the car park where his car was waiting for them.

'It was good of Hermione to bring the car,' he said. 'With Barbara away, I thought we might have to take a taxi to my Athens house.'

'Do you have a house everywhere?' she asked with a trace of sarcasm in her voice.

'I suppose you would say so,' he answered. 'Cheer up, you will soon grow used to us.'

'But will your friends grow used to me?' she countered. The slight stress of the word friends turned it into an insult, but she couldn't help that. Their encounter with Hermione had shaken her more than she liked to admit.

He shrugged. 'Hermione need not worry you,' was all he said.

'She doesn't!' she retorted.

He lifted an eyebrow, unlocking the car before opening her door for her. 'If she doesn't, you should be more careful of the impression you give to my friends,' he bade her before shutting the door on her. 'It will be all over Athens that you are less than sure of your power over me. If you had wanted Hermione to think you a secure and happy bride you could have cut her out with the greatest of ease. You had only to take the first step forward yourself and I would have followed your lead with pleasure.' The door didn't shut properly the first time and he opened it again, slamming it so hard that the car rocked on its axis.

'She would have told all Athens something un-pleasant whatever I did,' she said as Demis got into the car beside her. 'It was obvious that she didn't like me.'

'She didn't have to.'

She opened her eyes wide. 'Why not? Don't you want your friends to like me?' There was the slight stress on friends again, but she cared even less than the first time.

'Not the Hermiones of this world. She wouldn't have come if she had known I had you with me. I told you, you don't have to worry about her.'

'Because she's in love with you?'

He put his hands on the steering-wheel. The sun shone full on them and they looked more golden than ever—and very strong. Emily's heart beat a tattoo of sudden panic and she looked down at her own hands, noting how white and soft they were against his.

'Are you jealous because she knows what my kisses are like and you do not?' he asked.

'Certainly not!' Emily's lips tightened into a disapproving line. 'But she certainly wanted me to know that you had kissed her,' she told him. 'And that you'd enjoyed it too!'

'I did.'

'Then why didn't you marry her?' Emily demanded.

'Because I didn't have to, if you want to know.'

'Not even to gain control of her father's airline?'

She saw the angry tilt to his face and shivered with a fear she had never known before. She would have recalled the taunt if she could, but it was too late for that.

'My wife,' he said in measured tones, 'needs more than mere material possessions to become mine. Hermione fell short of those ideals. Does that satisfy you?'

She nodded her head blindly. 'You didn't have to tell me that.' She pulled herself together with an effort. 'But you have to admit that your wife had to bring you a sizeable dowry all the same. You may not have married Hermione for her possessions, but you didn't marry me for my kisses either!'

'Are you sure?'

It was so quietly spoken and so—so menacing! What had she done? She was alone and at his mercy if he chose to—— It was a pity she hadn't thought of that before! She looked straight ahead of her, very close to tears. What with getting married the day before and the four-hour flight from Heathrow today, it was no wonder that she was on edge. But would he realise that? And would he make allowances for her having an attack of the jitters when she should have been at her very best, just about to meet his family for the first time?

'I'm sorry,' she said. 'I shouldn't have said that—any of it.'

'Why not, if you thought it was the truth? You usually say what you think, don't you?'

'Not to you.'

He turned his full attention back to her. 'Now, I wonder why that is?' he said thoughtfully. 'Could it be that you have something to hide?'

She was indignant. 'Of course not! You know everything there is to know about me!'

A muscle moved in his cheek. 'Not yet I don't,' and Emily was only too conscious of his hidden meaning. 'But I mean to know you inside and out before I'm through.' He put up a hand and brushed the angry tears from her face. 'Destiny calls, my love. It's nothing to cry about.'

'I'm not your love!' she denied with a return of spirit. 'Don't—don't pester me, Demis!'

His hands grasped her by the shoulders, pulling her firmly into his arms. She struggled against him, hitting out wildly, but he was never in any danger of losing control of himself—or her.

'It's time you learned something about me, sweetheart,' he said in her ear. 'Nobody, but nobody, gives me orders. Certainly not a slip of a girl who doesn't know which way she's looking. Is that clear?'

She nodded. 'But——'

His eyes glowed. 'But? But I'll pester you whenever I want to!'

'You will not!' she declared. 'You promised——'
But she never finished her sentence. His mouth came

down on hers and he held her more tightly than ever against him. For a breathless moment she was very frightened. She had always known he was strong, but her own weakness in the face of that strength was a revelation to her. Her lips parted beneath his, against her will, presaging a momentary response to his ardour that shook her to the roots of her being. Humiliation welled up inside her as he finally released her, putting her back into her seat beside him.

'You promised you would leave me alone,' she said huskily. She sounded like a small, repentant child, unsure of how to make amends to a threatening adult.

'All the time you wanted me to,' he replied.

'I do want you to!' she claimed.

'Then you'd better not tempt me to break my word again,' he answered harshly. 'You can be the only loser if I do.'

'But I didn't!' She swallowed hard, very aware of her recent moment of weakness. 'Did I?' she couldn't resist adding.

'You're a walking temptation!' The abrupt reply was completely unexpected. 'And I suspect you know it. How right I was when I said you'd be a thorn in my flesh. A Thorne by name and a thorn by nature!'

It was on the tip of her tongue to tell him that many thorned plants produced the prettiest flowers, but the unwisdom of such a remark was apparent even to her.

'Thorns only prick you if you grasp them,' she said instead. 'You had better keep your hands to yourself.'

'Some defences are only meant to be overcome,' he

told her dryly, 'and, as I like a challenge as much as the next man, you'd better keep your prickles out of sight.'

She pretended not to have heard him, 'Hadn't we better be going?' she suggested.

His eyes travelled over her face and down over her figure. She was sharply reminded of the way he had looked her over on the train and how much she had resented it.

'Very well, *korítsi*. For now, you will have your own way. Lunch is waiting for us at my Athens house and, after that, we have a long drive to Nauplia where my brother and sister are waiting to meet you. It is at Nauplia that I prefer to live when my work doesn't call me away elsewhere. It is the most beautiful of all my houses.'

'I see,' she said in a strained voice. 'Will I live there all the time?'

His eyes swept over her again. 'That depends on you,' he said.

The Athens house was one of the old ones left beside the ancient Greek and Roman market places. From its windows the Acropolis dominated the scene with its constant reminder to the modern city that it owed its existence to the old-time gods who even now exacted their due from its citizens. Mighty Athene no longer had her statue in the temple that had been built for her glory, and Poseidon, the blue-haired god of the sea, no longer had to be pacified for losing the city to the goddess of wisdom, but their stories were recounted daily to the swarms of tourists who came to Athens only because of them. Their appeal was as great now as it had ever been at the height of their powers. Theirs was the voice that beckoned to all Europe to return to its beginnings by making a pilgrimage to Greece.

Emily fell in love with the house at first sight. She loved the crumbling pantiles with their traditional decorations; the casement windows, carefully shuttered against the light; and the decaying elegance of the watered-silk hangings on the walls. Most of all, she was taken with the astonishing assortment of antique furniture that rubbed shoulders happily with the artefacts of centuries. There were several pieces of statuary, but she didn't know enough about the art to tell if they were any good or not.

'Where did they come from?' she asked Demis. She had been conscious that he was watching her.

'I bought most of them in Italy,' he answered. 'Whenever they came on to the market.'

'Why Italy?'

'They shipped our statues there by the thousands. Why shouldn't I bring a few of them back where they belong?'

It must have been a very long time ago, thought Emily. 'Do you mean Imperial Rome? Julius Caesar, Nero, and so on?' And when he nodded, she asked him, 'But couldn't they carve any statues of their own?'

His glance was wry. 'They tried,' he said. 'But the genius wasn't there. Only the Greeks had that. The Roman contribution was to polish their works to give them a soapy look—like this one over here.'

There was a difference, she saw. The older statues glowed with the life of the marble from which they were created. Beside them, the others looked insignificant, more like very good plastic copies. Poor Rome, she thought. The whole world had been at their feet, but their jealousy of the greater civilisation of Greece had been a constant irritant to them. They had ruled the whole known world, or the greater part of it, but they had initiated very little in the spheres where men have found their greatest inspiration.

'Which is your favourite piece?' she asked him.

Demis gave her an amused, knowing look. 'It isn't here, but in the house at Nauplia. It's a copy, as a matter of fact, of a piece in the National Museum. I'll show it to you this evening.'

Emily was impressed by the quality of the food with which they were served at lunch. She had always heard that Greek food was Turkish food not quite so well cooked, but Demis Kaladonis evidently expected high standards of cuisine in his establishments. Perhaps that was why he had married her? She could not repress a smile at the thought.

'I feel better with all that food inside me,' she told him. 'It's a long time since I ate a meal I haven't cooked myself and really enjoyed it. I shall grow fat if I always eat so much.'

'If you also grow contented I shall not complain. It will be good for you to have nothing to do for a while but enjoy yourself. If you do that, I shall be well pleased.'

She eyed him covertly from beneath her lashes to see if he was serious. How little he knew himself, she thought. At the first hint of her striking out in anything that he disapproved of, he would soon destroy her enjoyment in it. That much she had already dis-

72

covered about him. No, Mr Demis Kaladonis, I don't like you at all! she told herself, eyes lowered. And I like you least of all when you seem to think you have some kind of God-given right to rule my life.

But this did not stop her taking pleasure in the drive to Nauplia. Even in the wintry sunshine the tawny hills were redolent with a life of their own. It was not surprising that the ancient Greeks had seen gods and other strange beings wherever they had looked. There were moments when she, too, felt that if she turned her head quickly she would catch a glimpse of something strange and not for mortal eyes.

They went past the Monastery of Daphni, which had previously been a temple of Apollo, and past the ancient sanctuary of Elefsis, where Demeter had given corn to the world and had taught men how to sow and reap the crops in their due seasons. Demis pointed out across the water to where the sea-battle of Salamis had been fought, the turning point in the war between the Greeks and the Persians. He made it sound as though it had happened just the other day, that if he had not seen it with his own eyes, his grandfather certainly had. It gave time a longer perspective than Emily was accustomed to, and she felt her first glimmer of pride in the people she had married into more or less by accident.

'Do we pass over the canal at Corinth? I've always wanted to see it,' she confessed. 'Wasn't it cut by the same French company that did the Suez Canal?'

'They planned it and began it,' he conceded. 'There were too many land-slips for them to finish it. It was a Greek company that did that. Before, the Corinthians used to haul the ships up manually and let

73

them down on the other side of the isthmus. It was how they made their living. They never wanted the canal to be built for that reason. Not that that stopped many people from trying. The Roman Emperor Nero thought to immortalise his name by cutting the canal. He even dug the first few spadefuls himself, and that was his undoing. The very ground wept blood where he had put in the spade.'

Emily remembered the story when she saw the straight, sand-yellow sides of the narrow cut that divided the northern part of the mainland of Greece from the southern part, the Peloponnese, sometimes called the Morea because its shape is somewhat reminiscent of a mulberry leaf.

Demis stopped the car by the canal and bought her a can of fruit juice to drink. Emily would have liked to have spent longer, staring down at the clean sides of the canal, just in case a ship should pass through it while they were there, but she could feel her husband's impatience to be gone and turned reluctantly back to the car.

'There will be other times,' he said, closing her door on her. 'We are not very far from Nauplia now.'

But it seemed far to Emily. Darkness fell and a chilly wind sprang up, making her glad of the protective warmth of the car. She snuggled further down into her seat and allowed her head to lean against the high back, shutting her eyes for a few minutes. The next thing she knew she was being shaken awake and Demis was leaning over her, his face as stern as ever.

'Wake up, *korítsi*, we're home!'

'Home?' She managed a confused smile. 'Oh, you mean we're at Nauplia.' She sat up quickly, embarrassed that he should have seen her sleeping. Her hand went up to her hair and she patted it, aware that she was not looking her best. 'You promised to show me your favourite statue,' she reminded him, to cover the awkwardness of the moment. 'I'm expecting something wonderful!'

'Come on then,' he bade her. He put a hand beneath her elbow and hauled her out of the car and on to her feet. 'You can see it on the way through the hall, and then you can have a wash before you meet my family.'

She nodded, wiping the sleep out of her eyes. She felt crumpled and a mess and she blinked in the sudden light that came flooding out when he opened the front door.

There was no escaping the sculpture after all. It stood as high as she did in the centre of the enormous marble-floored hall. The nude woman representing the goddess Aphrodite was one of the most beautiful and the most detailed she had ever seen. Accosting the goddess was Pan, his intentions obvious, and round their shoulders circled a cupid-like figure whom she took to be Eros. That Pan was not going to win the goddess was made plain by the way she held one of her sandals in her hand, ready to punish him in the way that comes most naturally to women of the eastern Mediterranean, who will whip off their shoes as quick as thought as the nearest and handiest weapon in any quarrel.

'It's very frank,' Emily said at last, feeling called upon to make some comment. 'Though she's very lovely.'

He was looking at her inscrutably. 'You could have

75

modelled for her if you had your hair done differently.'

She gave him a quick look. 'But she's——' She broke off, not liking to give him further cause for embarrassment by mentioning the beautiful proportions of the goddess's figure. 'You couldn't possibly know that!' she added with mounting indignation.

'Of course I know,' he said. 'I have seen women before and I can imagine very well what you look like.' He caressed the marble figure, giving her a familiar pat on the behind. 'One day you'll show me if I'm not right! But now you will wish to see the rest of the house and meet your new relations.' And he added something else in Greek that she didn't even try to translate. All she could think of was that she would have to pass that statue every time she came into or went out of the house.

CHAPTER FIVE

THE sharp knock at the door disturbed her dreams and brought her reluctantly into the present moment. She opened her eyes and was astonished to see her husband's tough shape outlined against the french windows that led out on to the balcony. There had been no request from him to come into her room. Well, if he thought he could come and go as he pleased, he had another thought coming! She opened her mouth to tell him exactly that, when he made a compelling gesture demanding her silence.

'*Oríste!*'

The door opened to the sound of rattling china, and a maid appeared, carrying a heavy tray laden with coffee and rolls for two.

'*Kaliméra, kyría, kyrie,*' the maid said, a distinct gleam in her eye. 'You slept well, yes?'

'Thank you,' Emily murmured, wishing them both elsewhere and herself back asleep. Her husband said something in Greek to the girl, who smiled at him worshipfully and withdrew with a stifled giggle.

Emily frowned across the room at him. 'I wish you wouldn't make jokes at my expense to the maids,' she said. 'And what are you doing in my bedroom anyway?'

He walked towards her, the expression on his face giving away nothing. He poured some coffee into a cup and added some sugar with a careless hand. 'You are my wife.'

'I won't have you coming and going as you please!'

'Would you prefer them to think that you have no attraction for me—or draw the conclusion that you are not womanly enough to want to please your husband? It is not I they will blame if they see that we are less than happy.'

'It isn't any of their business!'

His eyebrows rose. 'That will scarcely prevent them from speculating on your motives for excluding me from your bedroom. Most Greeks would think poorly of such an arrangement.'

'Even if there is no love lost?'

'Let us say we are more realistic about marital relationships than you appear to be, Emily *mou*. I had no idea the English were such a romantic people. We are always being told about the permissive ways of the northern nations, but you are different, I think? What do you expect, my Thorne? That the man of your dreams will carry you away from me on his snow-white charger and that you will be happy ever after? If you wish to be a truly romantic heroine you must accept the adventures that come your way.'

Emily gave him a steady look. 'I'm not in the least romantic,' she said. 'I leave that sort of thing to Margaret and my mother—and to Patrick when he's in the mood.'

His evident amusement made her angry. 'The practical approach would make you accept me as your husband in every way,' he told her. 'In Greece such marriages are common. We begin with friendship and allow love to grow with the years.'

'But we *aren't* friends!' she retorted.

78

'Have you thought why that is?'

She shook her head. 'I try not to think about you at all,' she informed him roundly. She poured herself out a cup of coffee, seeing that he had no intention of doing so, and tried to keep her hands steady as she did so. She knew, even while she refused to so much as glance in his direction, that he was staring at her in that peculiarly masculine way he had, and she drew the sheet higher up around her shoulders in a defensive movement that was as old as time.

'If you hurry with your breakfast we will have time for a swim before I start work.' His eyes gleamed with a sudden amusement. 'Aphrodite reunited with the waves should be a sight to see!'

'I don't feel like swimming,' she said.

'Why not? Don't you want me to see you splashing around, afraid to go out of your depth?'

The anger that he roused in her so easily made her answer before she had thought. 'I can swim as well as anyone I know! Shouldn't you be looking to your own laurels?'

'I'll meet you in the hall in half an hour,' he challenged her. 'If you are as good as you say you are, I may even allow you to go swimming by yourself when I am not on hand to rescue you if you get into trouble. The sea is only dangerous here when there is a storm in the offing, and then none of us go into the water.'

'I'll meet you in the garden,' she compromised.

His glance was distinctly mocking. 'How easily embarrassed you are,' he observed. 'Do you want me to put clothes on my statues as the Victorians did in England?'

'I don't care what you do.'

'Not even if I change my mind and make love to you instead of taking you swimming?'

She drew the tray closer to her, shrugging her shoulders. 'It takes two to make love,' she declared with a confidence she was far from feeling.

He bent over her, kissing the curve of her cheek with gentle lips. 'Don't make the mistake of underrating me, little Emily,' he warned her. 'So far I have agreed to allow you to call the tune, but I can command you any time I choose and you will have no choice but to obey me.' He kissed her again, this time on the mouth, and sauntered out of her room, whistling softly beneath his breath.

Oh, how she hated him! She could have thrown the pot of coffee at his head with the greatest of ease. What right had he to threaten her? And what about him underrating her? He would not find it half as easy to treat her to the masterful approach as he seemed to think! She had a mind of her own and a tradition of independence he would find hard to shake. She was not one of his sisters to submit tamely to his dicta just because he was a man!

Yet Chrisoula, his younger sister, had been overjoyed to welcome him home the night before. At sixteen she was far more self-possessed than Emily had been at that age—or was now, when she was in her husband's company, she admitted with a wry honesty. Chrisoula had laughed out loud as soon as she had seen Emily.

'Ah, now we know what you have been doing in England!' she had teased her brother. 'But of course! Emily is as close as you will ever come to your ideal, as anyone can see. No wonder you brought her back to Greece in such a hurry!'

'You must ask her why she came,' her brother had said, his eyes on Emily's startled face.

'Did you give her any choice?' Chrisoula had demanded, wide-eyed. She had embraced Emily with a warmth that had surprised the English girl, determined to make much of her. 'If I know you, you carried her off to Greece without a by-your-leave and didn't care whether she wanted to come or not.' She hugged Emily all over again. 'Was that how it was? You can tell us, you know. We have all suffered from Demis' high-handed ways!'

Almost Emily had told her the truth, but something had prevented her. 'No,' she had said. 'I wanted to come: Demis would have had a hard job leaving me behind in England.'

'Then perhaps it is that you are tired?' Chrisoula had persisted.

'Or because we had a tiff on the way here,' Demis had told his sister, his eyes fixed on his wife's face. 'The English may pretend to be cold, but this one is as jealous as any Greek girl.'

Chrisoula had seemed delighted at this suggestion. 'But what had you to be jealous about?' she had demanded.

Emily had shot Demis a speaking look. 'Your brother likes to have his joke,' she had said in freezing tones.

Demetrios, Demis' younger brother, had been less curious than his sister. If anything he had been bored by Emily's arrival and he had gone out straight after the evening meal without a word to anyone.

'You must miss Barbara and Giórgios when they are away,' Emily had said to him.

'I don't mind,' he had answered. 'Barbara is apt to fuss over me. That's the trouble with elder sisters.'

Emily had taken the hint. 'I have an elder sister myself,' she had told him, 'but I can't say she fusses exactly.'

'Then you're lucky. Barbara could hardly bring herself to go with Giórgios in case anything awful happened in her absence.' He smiled suddenly. 'She'll never forgive Demis for bringing you here while she's away.'

But Emily had been glad she had been away. It had been enough of a strain meeting the two younger members of the family and finding her way round the huge house that Demis called home.

It wasn't surprising that she had slept soundly when she had finally escaped to her bed, and now even that retreat had been taken away from her. It seemed that there was absolutely nowhere where she could be sure of her privacy from Demis. If she had dared she would have locked her door against him, but she was afraid of the consequences of such an action. She was more scared of the handsome, golden Greek she had married than she cared to admit.

There were only ten minutes of the half-hour left when, struggling with the reluctance that assailed her, Emily dressed herself in her swimsuit and donned the only beach-robe she possessed, made of coloured towelling and so short that it displayed the full length of her legs. Even pulled down as far as it would go, it had a saucy look that dismayed her. Accordingly, she went down the wide marble staircase, her belligerent

82

mood reflected in the eyes she carefully averted from the statue in the centre of the hall.

Demis was waiting for her at the foot of the stairs. His swimming trunks saved him from being as nude as the statue beside him and she couldn't help but be aware of the muscular strength of his body, his wide shoulders and narrow hips and the straightness of his deeply tanned legs.

Silently he handed her a freshly picked rose from the garden. The scent from it was heavy and seductive, quite unlike the overbred, showy blooms that had occasionally been presented to her in London. She took it from him, raising it to her face, and was surprised to find he had taken the trouble to remove the thorns from its long stem.

'Thank you,' she said shyly. 'I love roses. The more prickles the better the scent, someone once told me. Do you think it's true?'

'Maybe.' He watched her sniff the single scarlet blossom in her hand and shrugged his massive shoulders. 'Roses are like women,' he said. 'They are both better with their prickles removed.'

'I think that's rather trite,' she said.

'Do you?' He sounded amused. 'Perhaps because no one has tried to appreciate your scent at close quarters they have been content to be scratched by your thorns. I should not.'

The stem of the rose snapped between her fingers. 'The occasion will never arise. Besides, I should have some say in the matter, you know.'

'You have already had your say, *agapí*. Your future lies in my hands now.' He caught up the belt of her beach-robe and tied it more tightly about her waist. 'There are worse fates, *yinéka mou*, than falling in love with your own husband.'

'Never!' she exclàimed. She refused to meet his eyes and her gaze fell on the naked, marble form of Aphrodite. 'That creature and I may have more in common than you know!' she added, willing to use any weapon to wipe the assurance from his face.

'You have much in common,' he agreed, his hands on the lapels of her robe. 'What else do you have?'

'She liked variety,' she said. 'So do I!'

His bright, pale eyes looked deep into hers. 'In that case, I shall expect you to welcome me as your lover sooner than either of us thought. Why should you reject me if you welcome others?'

'Because I don't like you,' she whispered.

He stepped back from her, his hands on his hips. 'I could make you like me, Emily,' he warned her. 'Just as I could strip you of the thorns you seek to implant in my flesh by showing how empty your words are. I think my kisses are far from distasteful to you. Is that why you taunt me with words, Emily Thorne? Because you want me to notice you?'

She lifted her chin to show that she thought any such suggestion was beneath her contempt. '*I* taunt you? I think I've been remarkably restrained—in the circumstances!'

His expression was bland. 'Come and swim,' he said, 'and show me how like Aphrodite you are. I expect you will prefer to prove your claim to be a good swimmer rather than the one that you are a good lover—at least for today.' He took the rose from her hand and placed it on Eros' flying, chubby body with a mocking look at her over his shoulder.

'I never claimed to be a marvellous lover,' she replied.

'Comparisons with the goddess of love should never be lightly made. She may well find a way to punish you for taking her name in vain.'

'Stuff and nonsense!'

He put a finger across her lips. 'Hush! Are you as intrepid as you pretend, or merely foolhardy? Do you think she doesn't know that for two pins you would banish her statue to some forgotten corner of the garden where I can no longer compare your charms to hers? She likes to be admired by the men who are close to her.'

'Well, I don't.'

'That, my dear, is obvious.'

She liked that even less than she had liked his previous comments. For a long moment she battled in silence with the sense of chagrin that he should say such a thing, bitterly conscious of the bright, inquiring look with which he was regarding her.

And then as the silence between them lengthened, he added, 'Never mind, I can wait. You feel more of a woman today than you did yesterday, and who knows how you'll feel tomorrow?'

'I'll feel just the same about you,' she said. 'I don't like you.'

'But you're coming swimming with me?'

'Oh yes!' Her eyes glinted with temper. 'If you can keep up with me in the water. You won't have the same advantages as you have on land, you know. Brute strength won't get you very far when you're out of your depth!'

'We'll see,' he said. 'Don't try me too far, *yinéka*

85

mou!'

Yinéka mou, Emily repeated to herself, and came up with the unwelcome translation of 'my woman'. She would never be his woman, whatever he might like to think. She belonged to nobody but herself and that was the way she intended it to be always. Only, as he showed no signs of listening to what she said, not really listening, she despaired of ever ramming the fact home to him.

'When I have my own restaurant——' she began in an unnaturally high voice, '—and I shall have it sooner or later, I've made up my mind to that, whatever you may say!—I shall try to reflect some of this sunshine and light in the decor. The light in Greece is beautiful at all times of the day.'

He sauntered through the garden ahead of her, his towel thrown carelessly over one shoulder. 'So, you have found something to admire here? It is said that it is the light that makes the Greek so aware of physical beauty. Our buildings need the sun—and so do our people. You won't find it easy to box it up and transport it to England. It will pull you back to Greece and to me, you see!'

'To Greece perhaps,' she murmured.

The swinging ease of all his movements was attractive to her, though. If she hadn't known him as a person, she would have enjoyed watching him, she thought. She liked the gold of his skin and the hardness of his body. Did he move as well in water? she wondered. She hoped not. There had to be something she could do as well as he, if not better. She had never doubted her own capabilities before, so why should she now?

When they reached the beach, which was practically inaccessible except from the few houses that surrounded it, Demis dropped his towel on the dark brown sand and began to run towards the water. Emily followed more slowly, removing her robe as she went. She had a sudden, unreasonable fear as she entered the sea that there would still be turtle-like animals in the water who fed on human flesh, as there had been in the days of Herakles, or Hercules as the Romans had called him. But, if there were such beasts, there was no sign of them in the blue waters that frothed deliciously about her ankles.

As soon as it was deep enough to swim, she cast herself off, losing herself in the ecstasy of the feel of the water on her body. There were no doubts and difficulties left to prey on her as she exulted in her own powerful strokes, taking her ever further from the shore. The pull on her muscles, the rhythm of her breathing, all served to add to the exhilaration of the exercise her body had been starved of for so long. It was cold too, she belatedly realised, even here in Greece, much colder than she would normally have considered suitable swimming weather, and yet she herself was completely warm and happy.

She saw that Demis was still ahead of her and allowed herself to sink to the bottom, coming up underneath him and dragging him down with her. That would show him that he was not as omnipotent as he imagined! She released him and swam vigorously for the safety of a sheltering rock, but he was quicker than she had allowed for and, grasping her by the nape of her neck, he pulled her close up against him, his arms encircling her struggling figure. Try as she would, she could not escape him.

'Demis, I want to go back. I'm cold!'

'I could warm you——'

'I'm going back!'

He released her at once and she swam as fast as she could for the shore, then ran as hard as she had ever run from the touch of his hands and the aura of masculinity he seemed to wear like a cloak about him wherever he was. Her robe seemed an ineffective defence, but she shrugged herself into it, tying it tightly about her. It was ridiculous to go swimming in January, she considered. No wonder she was cold —ice cold, as if she were suffering from shock.

Demis came more slowly after her. She eyed him from under her lashes, hoping that she could handle the situation.

'That's the last time I swim until next summer! I can't think why I allowed you to persuade me——'

'You weren't cold until you saw you couldn't get the better of me,' he retorted calmly. 'You don't like being touched, do you, Emily *mou*? Why not, I wonder?'

'I don't like you to touch me!' she retorted.

He picked up his towel and rubbed himself down vigorously. 'Because you might have to give a little in return?' he questioned her. 'Must you guard your independence so drastically?'

'If I don't, who else will?'

'It depends how important it is to you,' he returned. 'It would be a pity to give up your real destiny for a mirage. It's not I who threaten your independence, but your own womanhood. Think about that for a while, Emily Thorne. It's not a restaurant you're needing, but a husband and children of your own.'

'I've got a husband,' she reminded him, making a face.

'Not yet you haven't!'

She turned her back, closing her eyes, shutting out the male taunt in his voice. Did he think her position was an easy one?

'Have you, Emily?'

His arms enclosed her against his chest, his hands linking together across her breasts. 'A husband would touch you whenever he felt like it, *korítsi mou*, and there would be nothing you could do about it, except to welcome him into your arms.'

'My husband will only come to me when I want him to!' she defied him, trembling a little.

'He'd be a poodle, not a husband, to allow that!'

She put her hands on his, trying to undo his clasp, but her strength was puny compared to his. As fast as she wrenched one finger apart, another closed against her. He blew on the back of her neck and turned her to face him. The lines at the corners of his eyes crinkled as if he were looking into the sun, but there was no clue in his face as to what he was thinking.

'Let me go!'

'I am no poodle, Emily. Did you think I was?'

'Let me go!'

'When I am ready, not before. What are you afraid of?'

'You're hurting me!' she declared with a burst of spirit.

'Am I? Think again, *agapí*. You are hurting yourself! Are you still cold? No, I thought not. Will your lips be cold too, or will they rejoice in the warmth of

mine?' He bunched her hair in his hand and pulled
back her head to meet his kiss. His mouth was hard
and demanding, searching for a response as avidly as
his hands explored her frame, cupping her breasts and
pulling her hips close against his own. His whole attitude was one of command, intent on bending her to
his will, but she wouldn't give him the satisfaction of
breaking. He was not her master and he was never
going to be—not if she could help it! Yet all pre-
tence at resistance faded from her mind as his kisses
changed tempo and took on a more seductive note,
moving from her mouth to her throat and back again.

'You are mine, Emily.' She heard his voice as
though from a distance, as he went on in a rush of
Greek which she didn't understand.

'No, no,' she pleaded. 'You promised, Demis.'

'Such a promise one makes to comfort a young
girl, but no woman would take it seriously. You were
not so foolish as to believe that I didn't intend to
claim my wife as soon as I was ready to do so, were
you?'

'Don't be silly!' Her voice caught in the back of her
throat and she felt weak at the knees.

'Now what does that mean? That you knew all
along you were destined to be my woman?'

She shook her head. 'I believed your promise,' she
whispered.

His only answer was to kiss her again, while she
clung to him to save herself from falling. 'And now?'
he asked her. 'What do you believe now?' His breath
was warm against her skin, making it impossible for
her to think of anything but him.

'I don't know!'

90

'There were other appetites you were meant to satisfy, my Emily, that appeal to me more than this restaurant of yours.' The barely concealed triumph in his words shook her to the core. It was his mouth, his voice, his arms, that were controlling her every movement now.

'Demis——' The moment was broken abruptly as Chrisoula's voice floated down the beach towards them. 'Demis! There is someone here for you! What's the matter with you? Are you both deaf? Demis, are you coming?'

Demis put Emily away from him, sheltering her from his sister's inquiring glance as the girl came running towards them.

'Who is it?' he called back. 'Tell them to come back later.'

'This one you will have to tell yourself,' Chrisoula declared. 'Hermione will never listen to anything I say.'

Emily felt a devastating feeling of pain within her. Hermione! What was she doing in Nauplia? Come running to her lover, no doubt!

'A promise is a promise,' she said in cool, brittle tones to her husband's back. 'I shall expect you to keep yours to me, Demis Kaladonis. I hate you, do you hear me? I hate you!'

His eyes were as cold as the English sea and much the same colour. 'We shall see,' he said. 'This isn't the time or the place to discuss our personal affairs. I'll see you at lunchtime. Chrisoula will take you into Nauplia if you wish to go——'

'I don't!'

He put up a hand and touched her cheek in a possessive gesture. 'There will be other times, *agapí*. You will need more than a little ice to keep me away from you now!'

Emily watched him walk away with stinging eyes.

'I don't like her either,' Chrisoula said with a shrug, 'but she has her uses as far as Demis is concerned.'

Of course she had! And Emily could have told her exactly what those uses were! At least she would have more pride than to allow him to use her in the same way. She was already appalled at the intimate way he had handled her, but she was quite determined that it would never happen again. She was more resolved than ever that she would leave him at the first possible moment and would open her own restaurant, anything that would allow her never to set eyes on him again.

'I must go and get dressed,' she said.

There was no sign of Demis at lunchtime. Emily could imagine him sharing his meal with Hermione in some restaurant, and humiliation burned within her. When he did finally come home and found her sitting, reading, in the garden, she barely looked up when he said her name.

'Emily, I have bad news,' he said. His tone was unaccustomedly gentle. 'Your father wishes to see me and I must fly to England immediately.'

She was on her feet, her grievance temporarily forgotten. 'I'll come with you!'

But he shook his head. 'He is in no danger. He wishes to get the transfer of the business tied up, though, so that there will be no difficulties if anything should happen to him. He has your mother to consider, *agapí*, as well as all of you.'

'But I want to see him!'

'Not this time, Emily. This time only I can put his mind at rest. You will wait in my house for me to come back to you——'

'As a Greek woman would, I suppose?' she shot back at him.

'As my wife must learn to do,' he amended. And he kissed her hard on the mouth. '*Yinéka mou*, it has a sweet sound to it,' he added.

'Has it?' she retorted. 'But I shall never be yours!'

But he was gone, leaving her alone in the garden with the book she had been reading lying where it had fallen at her feet.

CHAPTER SIX

EMILY went to Nauplia alone. She liked walking, and the distance between the Kaladonis house and the small town was well within her capacity. Although she had complained bitterly to Chrisoula about being forced to go swimming in January, she had been refreshed by the experience and, not for the first time, she regretted that she had had such limited time for exercise in London. At least she would have every opportunity for that in Greece.

Nauplia, she knew, had been the first mainland capital when the Greeks had been fighting for their independence a hundred and fifty years before. There were small signs of that former glory now, but it was a pretty place with one of the nicest harbours that Emily had ever seen and some pleasant souvenir shops which, she was to find, the Greeks stocked with more imagination than many host countries to the annual spate of holidaymakers from more northerly climes.

Since she was dressed in a pair of jeans and a pullover, there was nothing about her to proclaim her own nationality, and she was startled, when she sat down at a café overlooking the harbour, to be addressed in her own language.

'What will you have, madam?'

'A coffee,' she decided. 'Not Greek coffee, though.'

'Nescafé with milk?'

She nodded, relieved at the lack of difficulty of getting what she wanted. 'Thank you,' she said.

She was the only one there at first, sitting out in the wintry sunshine which seemed more than warm enough to her. She watched a *caique* coming into the harbour, admiring the clean lines of the boat. One day, perhaps, she would suggest to Demis that they should take such a boat all round the Greek Isles, stopping wherever the fancy took them and exploring where few people had ever explored before. She caught herself up hastily. Why should she want to go on such an adventure with Demis? She must be mad!

The coffee came and she paid for it while the waiter was there. What was Demis doing now? she found herself wondering. Was he already in an aeroplane, flying to England, to visit her family without her? Or was he lingering on the way to Athens, with Hermione by his side, an eager, expectant Hermione who would know all about his lovemaking in a way that she, his wife, never would.

Across the harbour was the miniature fortress of Bourtzi, which in its time had been put to some strange uses. Once, it had housed the executioner who had exercised his function on the prisoners who had been kept in the Palamidi fortress that rose high above the city; later, it had been a luxury hotel and, for all that Emily knew, it still was, though she wondered how the guests came and went from their favoured site.

She glanced about her, aware that she was no longer alone. The café had another customer, a man dressed in clothes that were the male counterpart of her own, who raised a languid hand in greeting as soon as he saw her looking in his direction. He heaved himself to his feet and came over to her table, grinning.

'I was hoping you would notice me,' he said artlessly. 'You don't mind if I join you, do you?'

'Not at all.' Any reservations she might have felt had been put to flight by the instinctive knowledge that Demis would have disapproved of such free and easy ways.

'I'm English too. My name is Keith Forest. I live in Birmingham.'

Emily smiled. 'Emily Thorne,' she supplied. 'Well, Emily Thorne Kala——' She broke off. It wasn't Kaladonis, she thought. She was almost sure that the feminine ending was something different. 'Emily Thorne,' she said again. 'I live in London—mostly. My family live in Kent.'

The young man eased himself into a chair, wincing a little as though he were stiff. 'This is the best time of the year to come to Greece, if you don't mind being cold and wet occasionally. I hate being one of the herd.'

Emily sipped her coffee. 'I went swimming this morning.'

'Did you? Walking is my thing. I walk everywhere if I can. It's the only way to see a country. I'm a bit out of training, as a matter of fact. I only started my holiday yesterday and it takes a little while to smooth the knots of a mostly sedentary job out of my muscles.'

'Few of us get enough exercise nowadays,' she agreed.

He leaned forward, looking pleased, putting his

96

arms on the table. They were white from lack of sun and not as strong looking as a certain other pair of arms. Emily blinked and averted her eyes.

'I'm glad I ran into you,' he said, sure that she had been equally glad to have him come over to her. 'We could go for one or two walks together, if you've nothing better to do?'

Emily bit her lip. What would Demis say to that? 'In the next few days?' she probed cautiously, for some reason feeling unaccountably guilty. 'I'd have to meet you in Nauplia itself. The people I'm with don't care for walking and they'd probably make some other suggestion for my entertainment if they knew.'

'You're staying with a Greek family?'

'My family knows them,' Emily explained.

'Well, that's all right with me, if that's the way you want it. I can imagine it might be rather trying for you having to fall in with their ways. The Greek girls I know seem to lead a pretty cloistered life, but I suppose they know their own countrymen best. A beautiful girl like you wouldn't be safe for a moment with any of them, that's how they'd see it. They don't know our English girls, do they?'

'Are we so special?' she asked.

'Most of you seem to know how to look after yourselves,' he said. 'I suppose it's all a matter of being used to standing on your own feet.'

Emily eyed him curiously. 'Are we any better off, do you think?'

He was surprised that she should ask. 'I should say so! Surely you wouldn't want to hand over your freedom to make your own decisions to anyone else?'

97

'No.' She sounded uncertain even to her own ears. 'But I think my sister would. She thinks her husband unmanly because he leaves all the decision-making to her. Or, at least, she often gives that impression.'

'Can't they decide things together?'

'In theory,' Emily agreed. 'In practise that often means that nobody ever decides anything. Perhaps, ideally, one should take it in turns.'

Keith laughed. 'Okay, that's how we'll arrange our walks. You can decide where we go the first time, and I the second, and so on. When will you be able to get away?'

'Tomorrow,' she said at once.

He smiled amicably at her. 'And where shall we go?'

She fluttered her eyelashes uncertainly in a gesture unconsciously borrowed from her sister. 'I don't know,' she confessed.

His smile grew wider. 'Epidaurus,' he suggested. 'You'll love it!'

Even to herself, Emily was not sure why she did not want to go to Epidaurus with Keith.

'No, not Epidaurus,' she said. 'We could walk to Tiryns, or take a bus to Mycenae, or even go to Corinth, but not Epidaurus. I don't want to go there.'

'Okay, lady, your wishes are my command. We'll walk to Tiryns tomorrow. I'll get my landlady to make up a packed lunch for the two of us and then we needn't hurry.' He put his hand over hers. 'It's made all the difference meeting you. I'm going to really enjoy this holiday! I can feel it in my bones.'

Emily wished she could feel a corresponding happiness at the prospect, but all she felt was a creeping despair that everything was always going to be too difficult for her to manage by herself in the future. She was behaving very badly, she knew. She ought to tell Keith that she was married, that she wasn't the simple English holidaymaker he imagined, but she didn't even know how to go about that. And she, if anyone, ought to know what that kind of deception could lead to, she thought with self-contempt. All her troubles had sprung from her pretending to be in love with Demis, and now it was only too likely that a similar disaster could overtake her because she was denying him.

'Keith, I don't just *know* this family I'm staying with. We're related—in a kind of way. You see——'

He gave her a kindly look. 'You don't have to tell me about it if you don't want to,' he cut her off. 'Family life is often complicated these days.' He stood up and smiled down at her. 'I'll see you here tomorrow at about nine o'clock. Will that suit?'

Emily never said a single word. She nodded her head and watched him walk away. If he didn't want to hear, there was no reason why she should tell him, she supposed. After all, it wasn't a real marriage. It wasn't as though she was really Demis Kaladonis' wife—or that she ever would be.

There was a certain amount of excitement in the Kaladonis house that night. Chrisoula said Barbara had telephoned to say that she and her husband would be back the following day.

'Oh? What time?' Emily almost hoped it would be at a time that would interfere with her proposed visit to Tiryns, but Chrisoula crushed that hope with an indifferent smile.

'Not until after dark. They won't expect us to meet them, unless you particularly want to. Demetrios is Barbara's pet. She doesn't have much time for me.' The girl didn't sound in the least sorry for herself, merely as if she was stating a fact about which there could be no possible argument. 'Demis has always been my special member of the family,' she went on. 'He has promised that when I'm eighteen he will find a husband for me. It's less than two years now and I worry sometimes that he hasn't begun to do anything about it.' The Greek girl turned to Emily, her eyes wide and pleading. 'Could *you* remind him, Emily, that I don't want to go on being Barbara's shadow for ever? I want a home of my own!'

'I don't suppose Demis would listen to me,' Emily said.

'Why not? Did you want a house of your own too —away from all of us? You haven't much hope of that, you know, until Demetrius and I are grown up. Demis takes his responsibilities as head of the family terribly seriously.'

Emily frowned, considering this. 'What about Barbara? Will she like me, do you think?'

'Oh yes! Barbara would like anyone who will stand between her and Demis. She's afraid of him, and so is Giórgios. Demis tries and tries to put them at their ease, but the more he tries, the worse it gets.'

'But aren't they much of an age?' Emily asked.

Chrisoula nodded. 'That's part of the trouble. He was just as particular about the way she behaved herself as he is with me, and then she walked in in the middle of one of his sessions with a girl-friend. She's treated him as though he has feet of clay ever since. And she doesn't like the girl he was with either.'

'But why should she mind so much?'

'She was in love with Giórgios and she didn't think much of there being one rule for Demis and another for her. She's awfully silly at times—as you'll find out.'

'I don't think much of that myself,' Emily commented.

Chrisoula laughed. 'You're bound to be jealous of Demis' other girl-friends,' she chuckled. 'But you don't have to worry, this one hasn't been in the lists since she went for Barbara like the shrew she is. Demis would have nothing to do with her after that.'

'How loyal of him!' Emily saw the young girl's shocked reaction to the sarcasm in her tone. 'I don't think you should tell me about Demis' other loves. Not that it matters in this instance. It's most unlikely that I shall ever meet her.'

'But you have met her! That was the awful thing. It wasn't just any girl, it was someone whom in other circumstances he might have married. Barbara thought he was going to marry her. That's what all the trouble was about. If he treated his fiancée like that, why shouldn't she have a little fun with Giórgios?'

'I see,' said Emily. 'It was Hermione Kaloyeropoulou, I suppose?'

'Of course. I told you Barbara is stupid. As if Demis would ever have married anyone so awful! Besides'—she gave Emily a droll look—'Demis would never marry a girl who had known other men, or who had allowed him to go too far before the

101

wedding. He would never be able to trust her, and that wouldn't suit Demis at all. He'd take what he was offered and marry elsewhere, which was precisely what he did. The funny thing is that I always thought English girls were so permissive these days, but I don't suppose you're really so very different from us after all.'

'No,' Emily agreed, 'I don't suppose we are. Though I can think of more desirable reasons for marriage than for my virtue,' she added dryly. 'I'd rather be loved, truly loved for myself.'

'You think Demis doesn't love you?' There was a glint in Chrisoula's eyes that was very reminiscent of her brother. 'Are you so difficult to love?'

This was not, Emily could see, the sort of conversation anyone should be having with a sixteen-year-old.

'You must ask your brother that,' she said repressively, and wondered why the Greek girl should be openly laughing at her.

'I will tell him that you have doubts,' Chrisoula teased her. 'That will put him on his mettle, *kuniátha mou*. He has the reputation of being a very good lover!'

Emily shrugged her shoulders. 'There are other things in life besides making love.'

'Oh, Emily, how quaint you are! You are so shy about the most ordinary things! No wonder Demis fell in love with you.' She sighed heavily. 'You must be missing him very much?'

Well, there was no point in pretending about that, Emily decided. 'Yes, I do,' she said.

The insistent ring of the telephone bell tore apart

the silence that had followed Emily's words. The two girls looked at each other, both of them startled by the interruption.

'Shall I answer it?' Chrisoula offered.

Emily nodded her head. 'It's probably for you anyway.' She watched the young girl cross the room, her carriage every bit as graceful as her brother's, though far more feminine. There was no one else she knew who moved in quite the same way as Demis did. They lacked the quick thrust and the imperative, male authority with which he surveyed the world.

'It's for you,' Chrisoula announced in flat tones.

Emily was taken aback. 'It can't be!' she exclaimed.

Chrisoula held out the receiver to her. 'It's expensive telephoning from England,' she reproved. 'Don't keep him waiting!'

Emily put the receiver to her ear. 'Demis?' she asked.

'Were you expecting it to be someone else?' his voice came back to her. 'One of those who provide the variety you claim to like so much?'

'I don't know what you mean,' she claimed.

'Good. For you have room for only one man in your life, *agapi*. Has that young sister of mine left the room?'

Emily looked round the room, a little surprised to find that she was alone. 'Yes.'

'You sound afraid. What do you think I can do to you over the phone? I thought you would be braver with a thousand miles between us!'

'I am quite indifferent to how far away you are! If I sound concerned, it's because I'm naturally worried

103

about my father—whom you won't allow me to see——'

'It's best for you to be in Greece, until you get used to things as they are,' he interrupted her. 'Your father is feeling better and we shall soon conclude our business together. He agrees with me that it is too soon for you to visit him. You would do better to prepare yourself for my return, Emily.'

'I shall never be a Greek wife, sitting at home, waiting to do my husband's bidding! You can't keep me here for ever.'

'You are the woman of my house now. It was agreed between us when you promised to marry me——'

'I didn't agree to anything of the kind!' she exploded angrily.

'Naturally you would not put it into words at that time. The agreement was between your father and myself that I should shoulder the responsibility for your future happiness.'

'And when do I have my say?' she inquired dangerously.

'We shall ratify the agreement together, where a man and woman should, in each other's arms.'

Emily felt weak at the knees. 'Never! You promised——'

'I promised you would not regret marrying me. Be practical, Emily, there is more to real life than the romantic notions you use as a wedge between us. Don't you know how much I want you?'

'As a woman, but not as a wife!'

'My dear girl, is there any difference? No, don't answer that now, but think about it—think hard,

104

think about yourself, and think about me too. It's impossible to argue with you over such a distance. Tell me instead what you have been doing today?'

How could she answer that? Should she tell him about Keith? she wondered, but she knew he would only forbid her to go walking with him, and he had no right to command her in anything. Somehow she had to make this clear to him before it was too late. Too late for what, she didn't bother to ask.

'I managed to amuse myself,' she said.

'With Chrisoula?'

'Some of the time,' she compromised, trying not to sound guilty. 'Barbara is coming home tomorrow,' she added quickly.

'Chrisoula is a safer friend for you, even if she is a bit younger,' he remarked. 'Don't let Barbara push you into trouble because of the ceaseless war she wages with me.'

'Why should she do that?' Emily countered, beginning to think she had more in common with Barbara than she had thought.

He sounded amused. 'Giórgios has let her get out of control, but I shan't make that mistake with you, Emily *mou*, so be warned and don't do anything foolish.'

Emily made a face at the receiver. 'Giórgios sounds nice.'

'He's very nice, but he has his own wife. He's not for you and he won't understand if you go out of your way to flirt with him that you're only getting at me, but I shall, and I shall act accordingly.'

'No wonder even your sister dislikes you!' Emily told him. 'You're so unbearably superior about everything and everyone! Why should Barbara be controlled by anyone? Can't she make up her own mind about the way she wants to live?'

'Only if it gave her any happiness. Wait until you've met her and then see if I'm not right. Meanwhile, dream of me tonight, my lovely Aphrodite, and I'll be home with you as soon as I can arrange things here. Shall I give your love to your family?'

'Yes, please do, to all of them.' She held the receiver so tightly in her hand that her knuckles turned white. 'And to Hermione too! She is there, I presume?'

There was an instant's silence. 'Jealous?' her husband asked her.

'Of you? You must be mad!'

'You have no need to be jealous of Hermione, *yinéka*. If you allow her to hurt you it will be your own fault.'

'Oh? How do you work that out?'

'She is not my wife,' he said with an amused tolerance that infuriated her. 'A happily married man has no need to seek the company of other women.'

'Demis Kaladonis, I hate you! Do you know that?'

'Emily Kaladonou, look into your heart again and then tell me that you hate me—if you can. Do you think I don't know when a woman is interested in me as a man? I knew with you when I gave you my seat on the train. Why do you try so hard to deny it?'

'Because I don't like you!'

His tongue clicked against his teeth. 'Never mind, I like you far too well to let you go. Don't you wish we were close enough to kiss now? Alas! I must go and speak some more with your father. Pleasant dreams, Emily *mou*!'

Emily put the receiver back in its cradle. How dared he cut up her peace in this way, when she couldn't even put him out of countenance by asking after Hermione? Well, he needn't think she was going to sit around and wait for him to come back to her like some tame mouse he had put in a cage and forgotten while he had more interesting things to do and other mice to play with. This was a game for any number to play. He had Hermione, but she had Keith Forest. It was a pity the Englishman didn't cut a more exotic figure, but he was easily managed and with very little encouragement she would have him eating out of her hand.

'See how you like that, Demis Kaladonis!' she addressed the silent telephone.

Emily could only wonder at her own ill-humour. The day was exactly right for walking, neither too hot nor too cold; and the scenery was all that could be desired even by those who were hardest to please. There was nothing wrong with Keith either. He knew exactly when to speak and when to be silent, he was able to tell her all about the place they were off to see, and he had supplied them with a picnic lunch that at another time would have made her hungry just to think about it.

No, the fault lay in herself. She had spent a sleepless night, working herself into a frenzy by inventing clever remarks by which she could have got the better of Demis on the telephone had she been more quick-witted, and had he fed her the right words for her to cap, thus putting him once and for all in his place.

Perhaps a restaurant wouldn't satisfy her ambitions when she had it. Not that she had ever intended it to be the whole of her life. She had always planned to marry and have children, but her future husband had been a nebulous figure who would have had little impact on the main tenor of her life. He had been nothing at all like Demis Kaladonis—

'You're not listening, Emily,' Keith complained.

'I'm sorry,' Emily said automatically.

'I said, if Tiryns was already a stronghold of a king when Perseus founded Mycenae, how come Perseus was said to have ruled over both places?'

'I expect he took Tiryns by force of arms. It must have been an enviable property in those days. Just look at those walls!'

The walls in question were of gigantic proportions. No wonder the ancient Greeks had thought them to have been built by that legendary race of beings, the Cyclops. Like most men they had been only too prepared to undervalue the technology and the ability of their own ancestors.

Emily trailed after Keith along one of the huge arched passageways, suppressing a strong desire to return to the sunshine away from the evocative atmosphere of oppressive disaster that clung to the massive rocks.

'Wasn't it from Tiryns that Herakles carried out the tasks that Eurystheus, the king of Mycenae, had imposed on him?'

'Was it?' Keith wasn't much interested in a story he couldn't believe in. For him, wars and rumours of wars were a much more satisfying subject to exercise

108

his imagination on. 'Think of it, that people who actually lived here fought alongside Agamemnon at Troy!'

'I've never thought that Helen was worth all the fuss,' Emily said dully. 'Why ever didn't they let her go—if that was what she wanted to do?'

Keith gave her a horrified glance. 'Are you serious?'

'Of course,' she maintained. 'You wouldn't plunge your whole world into a war over some woman, would you?'

Keith stared at her, his mouth working. 'I might. Things are different nowadays. I can think of some men who would, though. Perhaps they're more possessive than I am.'

Emily's eyes widened. 'Do you think it's a Greek characteristic?' she demanded.

'They're more old-fashioned than we are in their attitudes towards women. Henry VIII may have executed two of his wives for being unfaithful to him, but I can't imagine an Englishman doing that sort of thing today. It may be different here. Most of the Greeks I've met seem to think they own their wives, and a typical one would certainly have something to say if another man tried to take her away from him. I wouldn't much fancy being the erring wife, come to that!'

Emily shivered. 'I wouldn't like any man to think he owned me.'

Keith shrugged, his attention wandering to the western staircase that led up to the ruins of the palace on the top of the mound. 'Greek thinking is different from ours,' he said. 'One flesh and all that, you know.

You can still see many peasant women helping their men in their work. If a man needs someone to hold a piece of wood he is sawing, who better to do it than his wife?'

'Peasants, yes, but not other people, surely?'

Keith grasped her reluctant hand and pulled her up the staircase to the top with its tremendous view across the citrus orchards and towards the sea at Nauplia.

'What's your worry?' he said. 'You're not thinking of marrying a Greek, are you?' He caught her other hand and pulled her up hard against him. 'Like should marry like, if you ask me. You'd be much safer with an Englishman.' He smiled slowly. 'Don't you think so?'

Safer, perhaps, but it was too late for safety now. Emily released herself, veiling her eyes from his eager look.

'I wasn't thinking of myself at all,' she said.

CHAPTER SEVEN

EMILY shrugged herself deeper into her coat as the chill wind from the sea made her shiver. Nauplia harbour was as black as ink and the only sound was the soft sucking noise of the miniature waves as the tethered boats rose and fell by the side of the wharf.

'Trust Barbara to insist on sailing at night,' Demetrios said with disgust. 'What time is it now?'

Emily glanced down at her watch. 'Almost midnight,' she answered on a sigh. She was tired too. The walk to Tiryns had been a qualified success, but afterwards Keith had wanted her to go back with him to the room he had rented in the town and he had taken her refusal badly.

'What do you want from me?' he had asked her.

'Someone to walk with,' she had told him uneasily, and had not been entirely surprised by his mocking laughter. 'Truly, I don't know you well enough to—to——'

'D'you think you'll know me well enough by tomorrow?'

'Keith, I don't think you understand——'

'Oh yes, I do, pet. You're well on the way to becoming a tease, d'you know that? You're too old, and you've been on your own for too long, to be as shy and as inexperienced as you pretend.'

'Then we'd better not see each other again!' she had flashed back at him. If she had had a fraction of

Margaret's confidence, she had thought bitterly, she would have had him eating out of her hand instead of allowing him to tear her into little strips for his amusement. 'Why can't we just go walking with each other—as friends?' she had pleaded.

'My dear girl, have a look in your mirror and you'll see the answer to that! What have you got against the exchange of a few kisses?'

That had been the moment to tell him she was married, but she hadn't done so. Instead, she had managed to look almost as uncomfortable as she had felt, and had said firmly, 'I don't feel like it.'

'Okay. That's all you had to say,' he had answered. 'I'll be moving on then. Goodbye, Emily.'

She had stared at him, wide-eyed. 'But I want to go to Corinth tomorrow. I thought you did too?'

His mouth had worked in the way it had when he was thinking. 'I'll think about it,' he had said.

Even thinking about it now, Emily felt a vast impatience with the way she had handled the whole conversation. Why couldn't they be friends? Why couldn't they have had a nice, moderate relationship with no emphasis at all on the fact that they happened to belong to opposite sexes? Why all the screaming banner headlines, when the situation was merely that they were both English and were both at a loose end?

'I haven't much taste for romance,' she had told him bluntly.

'You're telling me!' he had retorted. Which had accentuated how different he was from Demis, she had thought, not without satisfaction. Demis treated her as though she were a romantic fool of the first water, with one eye on cloud nine and one on Mr

112

Demis Kaladonis, and her feet permanently several feet off the ground. He was the only person she knew who had ever seen her other than practical and every-day in her reactions to life.

She shivered again and exchanged glances in the darkness with her brother-in-law. 'I wonder why they didn't wait until tomorrow?' she said.

Demetrios laughed without much humour. 'You haven't met Barbara yet! She'd have had poor old Giórgios heading for home at the first opportunity the moment she heard about you!'

'But why? I'd still have been here tomorrow.'

'Barbara will think she should have been here to meet you.' Demetrios jumped from one foot to the other in an effort to keep warm. 'Didn't Demis tell you about her?'

'He didn't really tell me about any of you.'

Demetrios grinned. 'I guess he thought you could look after yourself. Chrisoula likes you well enough.'

'I'm glad,' she said simply. 'How about you?'

He shrugged. 'Demis always said he would never marry anyone but a Greek girl, so you were kind of unexpected. That's not to say I don't like you, but Demis is a jealous devil and I have no intention of getting on the wrong side of him. It's bad enough having Barbara putting his back up all the time.'

'Deliberately?' Emily asked.

His laughter was caustic. 'Of course deliberately! She won't allow he has any authority as head of the family——'

'Why should he have? She's married, isn't she? And of age?'

'Giórgios doesn't pretend to have any control over

113

her, so being married doesn't count.' She was glad that in the darkness she could not be sure of his expression. 'Giórgios isn't at all like Demis,' he said dryly. 'He doesn't mind submitting to petticoat rule—that's most of Barbara's problem, if you ask me. If Giórgios would only stand up to her she'd be as sweet as honey.'

Emily hunched up her shoulders, turning her back on him. 'You're more like your brother than I thought. Men don't have to rule the roost, you know. Sometimes we women like to take a turn at having our own way!'

Demetrios patted her kindly on the shoulder. 'I shall love to see you telling Demis what to do—about anything important,' he added. 'If you ask me——'

'I'm not asking you. Demis will have to learn to respect my independence, just as I respect his. My life is just as important as his.'

'But different,' Demetrios pointed out, refusing to be squashed. 'You do not wish to be a man, surely?'

'Of course not.'

'Then there is no argument. The trouble with Barbara is that she would like to be a man. She has no respect for her own sex. She resents Demis because he makes it clear to her she is a woman, even though he is only her brother, and Giórgios who is her husband does not!'

The lights of the yacht came suddenly into view. Emily sighed with relief. Whatever her family thought about her, she was looking forward to meeting Barbara. It would be nice to have another woman to talk to. Chrisoula was a darling, but she was only sixteen and she didn't share Emily's need to retire

114

inside herself where no one could disturb the even tenor of her essential individuality. Chrisoula welcomed the rough and tumble of having her ideas turned upside down, Emily did not—not all at once and with the devastating efficiency with which Demis went about it. With Barbara there would be other things to talk about. Nice, safe subjects that didn't matter to anyone but which lent a cosy atmosphere in which she could recoup her forces ready for the next encounter with Demis.

The lights came nearer, reflecting red and green and pale yellow a thousand times in the surface facets of the water. How beautiful it was! Emily didn't know what she had expected, but the clean, sweeping white lines of the yacht took her breath away.

'You should have told me!' she exclaimed, awed, to Demetrios.

'What did you expect? A local *caique*? Demis began with one of those, but he really goes for style when he can afford it.'

'The *caiques* have enough style for me! Great heavens above, what did it cost? It ought to have a millionaire to go with it!'

'It has Demis.'

That caught Emily in the pit of her stomach. Winded, she turned on her young brother-in-law. 'He can't be as rich as all that! What would he want with my father's firm——' She broke off, aware of the bad taste in discussing her *proíka*, much as she resented it, with Demetrios. 'Never mind, I expect it's a good business investment, or something like that.'

Demetrios only laughed. 'You're too good to be true, little English sister,' he teased her. 'Didn't you ask any questions at all about Demis before you married him?'

'I suppose not,' she said diffidently.

'I thought English girls managed their own affairs, asked their own questions, ran their own lives?'

Emily was glad of the covering darkness that hid her hot cheeks. 'I never thought—There wasn't much time—It didn't seem to matter!' she told him.

'You'd have taken him without a penny to his name, wouldn't you?' Demetrios discovered with a delighted laugh. 'Did you tell him that?'

Emily shook her head, but which question she was denying she preferred not to ask herself. 'At least we English are not as mercenary as you Greeks!' she retorted in triumph. 'We don't bother about dowries and settlements and all the things that govern your marriages!' Only she had allowed herself to be bought by Demis for her father's sake and that was mercenary enough, but it hadn't seemed like that because she hadn't gained anything at all.

The yacht slid into the waiting berth beside them with the minimum of fuss and bother. The gangway was lowered and made secure by a smiling matelot, and Demetrios and Emily lined up at the bottom for all the world as if they were two officials sent to receive some important delegation. The thought amused Emily, but all thought of laughter fell away from her when she saw his strained face as he waited for his sister to descend the steps towards them.

'Well, well, Demetrios,' a light feminine voice floated down to them from the deck. Barbara's English was as perfect as her brother's, but the accent was more American, the vowels broader than in Demis'

116

precise speech. 'I thought I could rely on you at least. Why didn't you tell me our brother is married, hmm?'

'There was no hurry for you to know,' Demetrios answered.

'Not when Demis had to go flying back to England at such short notice?'

She was very well informed, Emily thought. She looked up, trying to see her better, but all she could see was the faint outline of a thin, petite woman, who didn't move at all, but seemed prepared to wait there on the deck for ever.

'Hullo, Barbara,' she called up to her. 'I'm Emily. Demetrios said I could come and meet you——'

'Why not? It is your house now. Your yacht too, come to that. Did Demis tell you to be kind to the new poor relations of yours?'

'Of course not,' Emily disclaimed. 'I've been looking forward to your arrival. In fact, I couldn't wait to meet you! I was hoping we could be friends?'

'Friends?' Barbara repeated the word as if she had never heard it before. 'My dear, isn't that rather optimistic? Demis will never allow you to be my friend.'

Emily frowned. 'Why not?'

'I am what is known as a "bad influence". The only reason Demis tolerates Giórgios and me is because there was no one else to keep house for him when our parents died. He would have turned me out long ago but for that.' She turned her head a fraction of an inch. 'Wouldn't he, Demetrios? He can't be bothered to see to your daily needs, can he? He's so much better at handing down orders and interfering with anything we want to do!'

Demetrios coughed. 'You make too much of it, Barbara. He does what he thinks is best for us all.'

'Which was all right when we were children, but it's been a long time since anyone could have called me a child!'

Another shape joined Barbara's on the deck. *'Ti tréhi?'*

'The matter?' Barbara turned on him. 'Everything is the matter!'

Giórgios' English was less good than that of any of his wife's family. He put a comforting arm round Barbara's shoulders and talked to her in Greek. Emily could understand some of it, but not enough to be able to make out exactly what the trouble was.

'What is it?' she whispered to Demetrios.

'She says you've come to spy on her and that you probably hate her too.'

Perplexed, Emily put a tentative foot on the bottom of the gangway. 'May I come on board?' she called up.

The only answer was Barbara's mad dash down the steps, brushing past her on the way to the car. 'Let's get home, shall we?' She laughed harshly. 'I'll bet Demis was sick that you had to meet me the first time without him!'

'Why should he care?' Emily asked her. She was beginning to think that Barbara's trouble was nervous. 'He doesn't choose my friends for me.'

Barbara leaned forward. 'Get in!' she beckoned imperiously. 'Sit here, next to me. I want to talk to you.'

Emily did as she was told. Inside the car, with the door still open, she could see the Greek girl clearly

118

for the first time. She was not at all like Chrisoula to look at, and far less handsome than either of her brothers. She had a small, cramped face, with a sulky twist to her mouth and a grey look to her skin that told its own story of pain and illness.

'Barbara, I really would like to be friends,' Emily began awkwardly.

'With Demis' wife! My dear, you've got to be joking. Like Caesar's wife, *you* have to be above suspicion, and in Demis' eyes I'm the original scarlet woman. Didn't he tell you?'

'No, he didn't.'

Barbara screwed her head round to take a closer look at Emily. 'What made him marry you?' she asked with an abruptness that amounted to open rudeness.

'I don't know,' Emily admitted.

'Not a love match? How interesting.'

'My father's firm has always had connections with Greece. Demis is going to take it over,' Emily said before she could stop herself. 'My father hasn't been well and wanted to retire.'

'Ah! A business arrangement! That sounds exactly like Demis!'

Emily died a little inside. She was hardly aware of shaking hands with Giórgios when Demetrios brought him over to the car, or of the two men climbing into the front seats of the car and driving off to the Kaladonis house. Of course she had always known that Demis had married her for commercial reasons of his own. 'I wish he'd taken me with him to England.' Without thinking, she spoke her thought out loud. 'I mean, I would have liked to see my father too,' she added quickly.

'Have you been bored on your own?' Barbara drawled, smiling a little.

'She couldn't have been. She's been out all day,' Demetrios put in. 'Where did you go, Emily?'

'I walked to Tiryns. I like walking,' she claimed.

'On your own?' Barbara's eyebrows shot upwards and her whole expression was one of inquiry tinged with contempt. 'Surely not?'

Emily felt a moment's embarrassment at having to admit that she had not been alone, but she dismissed her reluctance to mention Keith as mere foolishness on her part. She had nothing to be ashamed of in seeking the Englishman's company. She might just as easily have gone walking with a member of her own sex.

'No,' she said with unexpected firmness. 'I went with an English friend of mine. He likes walking too.'

'He?' Demetrios and Barbara spoke as one, united for once in their disbelief.

Emily shrugged. 'Why not? He's very nice.'

It was Barbara who recovered first. She broke into Greek for her husband's sake, recounting what Emily had said. She sounded excited and suddenly very much alive. Emily heard Giórgios' swift negative in answer to whatever it was his wife had asked him. Barbara made a comprehensive sound of discontent and returned her attention to Emily.

'Does this friend of yours live in Greece?' she asked.

Emily shook her head. 'He's staying in Nauplia.'

'And do you plan to go walking with him again?'

Emily threaded her fingers together. 'I think so.

120

We want to go to Corinth. We'll have to go part of the way by bus because it's rather far——'

'You can borrow my car!' Barbara interrupted her. 'I shall be so glad for you to have it. It will cement our friendship if we can lend each other our possessions, don't you think? Friends always borrow from one another.'

Put like that, Emily didn't like to refuse. She felt a bit daunted at the prospect of having Barbara as a friend, although that was what she had herself wanted in the first place. She had hoped to find her as pleasant and as likeable as Chrisoula, and then they could have had a lot of fun together, but with someone as neurotic as Barbara she doubted she would manage to enjoy even the commonplace, inevitable brushes with her that sharing a house with someone entailed. It was a disappointment, but the truth was that she didn't like Barbara. She felt sorry for her, but she didn't like her at all.

'I don't know if Keith drives,' she said.

'Doesn't matter at all!' Barbara declared. 'You drive, don't you?'

'Well, yes,' Emily admitted. 'I hold a driving licence, but I've had very little practice. It isn't worth having a car in London. There's nowhere to park it.'

'You'll find very little traffic on the Corinth road. Of course you must have the car!' Barbara insisted.

Demetrios turned his head to look back at his sister. Emily held her breath, hoping that he was going to forbid her taking the car, but he said nothing at all. His eyes flickered over Emily's shape and he turned back again to the front.

'I'll have to ask Keith,' Emily said in a voice that

didn't sound like her own at all.

It was Giórgios who answered her. 'Demis would never give his permission for you to spend a day alone with another man,' he told her in his heavily accented English. 'Why not wait till he comes home?'

'Because Emily isn't as old-fashioned and prudish as you are,' Barbara answered for her. 'English girls don't allow their husbands to confine them at home and have all the fun by themselves. Demis will have to learn that, won't he, Emily?'

Emily uttered a laugh that caught in her throat. She doubted that she would ever be in a position to teach Demis anything. 'Keith is only a friend,' she said defensively. 'Thank you, Barbara, I'd like to take your car.'

Emily was unfamiliar with the gears of Barbara's French car. She managed to stall the engine twice on the short journey into Nauplia. If she had done it a third time she would have turned round and driven straight back to the house. As it was, her pride wouldn't admit such a course. She was obsessed by the thought of Barbara rocking with amusement at her cowardice and couldn't bear to give her the opportunity to despise her more than she already did.

It was unlikely that Keith would be waiting for her at the café after their exchange of the day before, which made her journey seem all the more ridiculous. If he was not there, what would she do? She pulled at the gear-lever hopefully and was relieved to find that she had finally mastered its eccentricities. It was quite simple after all, and only her own lack of confidence had prevented her from getting the hang of it earlier. If Keith wasn't there, she would go on to Corinth alone.

But he was there. He looked up, surprised to see her in a car when she drew up alongside him. She sat there in silence while he got in beside her, and then she said, 'I didn't think you'd be here. I thought you had better things to do?'

'I thought I'd give it another try,' he responded. 'If you came at all, I figured it would be because you see things my way after all.'

'But I don't! I like you, Keith, as a friend, but I don't want to have to fight you off the whole way to Corinth and back. I'd rather go by myself!'

His mouth worked as he tried to make up his mind what to do. 'What's the matter with you?' he said at last. 'Have you got someone else? Is that it?'

'In a way. I just don't go for that sort of thing.'

'Is it me? Is it that I don't happen to turn you on?'

If she agreed to that being so, she thought ruefully, she would hurt him badly. And yet it was the truth. Even to herself, she would not admit the true reason for her lack of interest.

She sighed. 'Are you coming on my terms, or not?'

'I'm coming,' he conceded. 'Only I don't promise anything.'

She let in the clutch and slid the car forwards, sighing again. 'Okay, but I can't mean anything to you. Not really. How could I, when we've only just met?'

'It doesn't take time.' He thumped his fist into the palm of his hand. 'It either happens—pow!—like that, or nothing happens at all. Obviously you've never come up against it at all. Where've you been all your life? In a convent?'

'The next best thing,' she admitted without resentment. She was barely listening to him. Her mind had flown to her first sight of Demis on the train. Was it that kind of attraction she had felt for him in that moment? Keith hadn't been talking about *love*, love was something different from the surface sexual attraction that was all he wanted to indulge in. One could feel that kind of attraction and not be in love at all.

She found she had been holding her breath, and let it go with a relief that was not only physical in its impact.

'Keith, let's enjoy Corinth for itself—please? We may never get there again, and it would be a pity to spoil it with any silliness.'

'Would it?' His voice was dry. 'If you say so, darling. I'll try to be good, but you're too pretty for me to ignore altogether. You might not mind half as much as you think if you let yourself go, do you know that?'

She set her mouth in a stubborn line. 'I know myself. Tell me about Corinth. I want to know everything there is to know about it.'

'Okay, I'll do my best. Will that do?'

She nodded and smiled at him. 'That'll do fine!' she said.

His best was pretty good. He managed to conjure up a wealth of detail about the people who had held the key to the two parts of Greece and who had thrived for centuries on the ancient enmity between the Spartans and the Athenians, stirring the pot whenever the two cities had shown any sign of friendliness and taking the gold of both sides to show themselves impartial. They had had a reputation for luxury and soft living which had lived on into the present day when most people only knew Corinth as the home of the so-called oldest profession in the world. Their ladies of easy virtue had been renowned for their loveliness and for the shoes they wore, the emblems on the soles of which left 'Follow Me' written in the dust of their footprints. Today, Corinth was the victim of earthquakes and tremors which had reduced a prosperous city to a small, insignificant town with little to recommend it to the modern youth of Greece.

As always, the ancient Greeks had chosen their site with superb flair. Acrocorinth, the high place above the city, had one of the best views in all Greece. It was possible to see some walls on the brow of the hill, but it would have taken far too long to climb up to the top, and Emily abandoned the idea with reluctance.

'Did every city have its acropolis?' she asked.

'Sure thing. Acropolis only means the high place above the city. For some reason the gods of mankind have always preferred the heights. Perhaps they found it easier to look down on mankind when they were naturally above them.'

'Maybe,' Emily agreed.

She parked the car with care near the entrance to the site and ran up the steps ahead of Keith, anxious to have her first sight of a place whose name had been familiar to her since childhood from the letters St Paul had addressed to the Christian community there.

The seven pillars of the Temple of Apollo stood braced above the rubble, magnificent in their desolation. They were of the Doric order, very plain and, which was more unusual, were each made of only one piece of stone instead of the more usual drums pinned together to make up the column. The temple must have dominated the city from the very beginning. It drew the eye towards it wherever one was standing.

'There are other things to see,' Keith told her as she set her face towards climbing up to the temple.

'We could see everything from up there,' she objected.

'Not the fountain of Peirene.'

She hesitated. 'Is that so special?'

'It is formed from the tears of the nymph Peirene. I think she is weeping for her dead son, or lover, or someone like that. Come, let me show it to you!'

Still Emily hesitated. She didn't want to leave the main concourse of the site where the other tourists gathered and discussed the various features of the ruins they could see. She didn't want to be alone with Keith in some damp hole, where she might not be able to escape if he insisted on kissing her, an intention she could see was still in the forefront of his mind.

'Please, Emily. I shan't hurt you, I promise you!'

He held out his hand to her and she put her own into it and allowed him to lead her away from the foot of the temple and towards the underground fountain. She held back when he wanted to go inside, however.

'I don't want to go in there,' she told him mean-

126

ingly.

'It doesn't matter,' he answered roughly. 'No one can see us from here!'

He tightened his grasp on her hand and drew her close up against him. 'You didn't really think I wouldn't kiss you, did you?'

'Yes, I did! Keith, I don't want to!'

'But I do!'

He was much stronger than she had suspected and she had no chance of escaping the hot kiss he planted on her own lips. She struggled to retain her balance, bringing her knees up sharply just as he stepped away from her.

'You fool!' she turned on him furiously. 'I told you I didn't want to!'

'I didn't believe you,' he admitted, a wry twist to his mouth. 'I only want to kiss you, Emily. What's so wrong about that?'

'Well, Emily?' An only too familiar voice interrupted icily.

Emily's blood froze within her. *Demis!* But it couldn't be—he was in England. 'I think you'd better introduce us,' he went on in the same cold, deadly tones.

Emily pulled herself together with difficulty. 'Yes, of course,' she muttered. 'Demis, this is Keith Forest. We—we came to see Corinth together. Keith, this is Demis Kaladonis.'

Keith held out his hand, a strained expression on his face. 'Kaladonis? Miss Thorne is staying——'

'Miss Thorne?' Demis repeated. 'Emily must have misled you, Mr Forest. She is Miss Thorne no longer. She is the Kyría Kaladonou, my wife. *Kaladonou,*'

127

he said again. 'Belonging to Kaladonis and therefore to me. Do I make myself clear?' He put a possessive arm about Emily's waist, putting himself between her and Keith. 'I shall be taking Emily back to Nauplia,' he added in the same inexorable tones. 'You can drive my sister's car back when you are ready, yes?'

'But, Demis, I want to see the Temple of Apollo——'

His arm tightened about her until she thought her ribs would give way under the pressure. 'You are ready to leave now,' he said. 'Now, at once!'

CHAPTER EIGHT

'I THOUGHT you were still in England.'

It was the first time Emily had spoken since Demis had practically thrown her into his car and had driven off without a single backward glance at Keith's stunned and fearful face.

'Yes, it is bad luck that I am not, isn't it?'

She wished she were not quite so afraid of him. 'You're angry, aren't you?'

'Yes, I am angry.'

'You have no reason to be.'

'We shall not discuss it while I am driving,' he cut her off.

'We shan't discuss it at all!' She raised her head. 'There is nothing to discuss!'

His eyes flickered over her resentful face. 'Perhaps you are right,' he conceded. 'There is no need for any discussion between us. It was my fault for not understanding what you meant when you said you were more like Aphrodite than I knew. Now that I do understand, I shall see that you have no further cause for complaint.'

Genuinely bewildered, she raised startled eyes to his. 'What has Aphrodite got to do with it?'

'Didn't you claim to share her liking for variety? That I cannot give you, but there seems no reason why I shouldn't enjoy what is, after all, mine for the taking. I am confident that you won't miss your other lovers once you have learned the joys of being mine.'

'You sound more than confident. I think you're horrible!'

He stopped the car and put a hand under her chin, turning her face to his. 'My dear Emily, if I wish to I can make you fall in love with me like that!' He flicked his fingers under her nose. 'And I think I do wish to. Why should I allow you to go on wasting yourself on others when I have a perfect right to have you for myself?'

She quivered beneath his touch. 'How do you know I've been wasting myself?'

'I didn't. I do now.'

'It isn't true,' she told him. 'I don't know why I said it now.'

'Don't you? Did you already know this boy-friend of yours then? Perhaps you meant it as a warning that I was making a fool of myself where you were concerned? But I shall not be made a fool of twice, as you will shortly discover!'

'He's not my boy-friend! He's simply someone I went walking with. You make me sound like a vulgar pick-up!'

'True.'

'But I'm not!'

'Aren't you? You forget that I saw you with him with my own eyes. You were not walking then! Indeed, it seems you were so anxious to have his company that you took Barbara's car so that you would not be obliged to walk at all. My sister is neurotic enough without you having to stress that you are the mistress now and that she has no rights at all. It would have been kinder to have asked her if you could take the car——'

'She offered it to me! Oh, don't believe me!' Emily added, seeing the hard, unreadable look in his eyes. 'Ask Demetrios. He'll tell you. Or Giórgios, he was there too.'

She could see that he didn't believe her. His expression remained as unyielding as ever, and she was well aware that this was no small misunderstanding which she could put right with a few words. This was something for which he would never forgive her, because he was Greek and, as far as the Greeks were concerned, their women appeared to hold their honour in their hands. Oh, she had not broken the rules in actual fact, but she hadn't given a thought to his precious honour when she had set forth with Keith for Tiryns, and even less today when she had driven him to Corinth.

'I'm sorry,' she said.

'So am I!'

'I won't admit that I've done anything to be ashamed of, though,' she said defiantly. 'Perhaps I shouldn't have gone alone with Keith, but not for the reasons you are thinking. I didn't know he thought of me as anything other than another English person he had met on holiday. He didn't mean anything more than that to me. I don't see why you can't believe me about that.'

'Your record for truthfulness is a trifle dubious, shall we say?' he replied. 'I wonder if you have ever told me the truth?'

She could only stare at him. 'What do you mean?'

'Do you want a list of the lies you have told? Very well. You said you had never heard of me before I

131

offered you my seat on the train. You told your
father you were deeply in love with me. You pretended an innocence you do not possess. You told me
the height of your ambitions was to have your own
restaurant when you are plainly determined to become a rich and idle wife, giving as small a return as
you can on the deal. And, on top of all this, you have
the nerve to pretend you are the quiet member of
your family, that games with the opposite sex are
something in which you refuse to indulge and for
which you condemn your sister—your mother even!
—while you are too busy working! It doesn't add
up to a very pretty picture, does it?'

Emily was appalled that he should believe such
things about her. 'If you think all that, why did you
marry me?'

'I wonder that myself.'

'Well, there is no reason why you should *stay*
married to me!' she shot at him, pride coming to
her rescue. 'We can have the marriage annulled. I
never wanted to marry you in the first place.'

'Didn't you?'

'That's what I thought!'

She would have done anything to have been able
to wipe that superior smile from his lips.

'Why don't you have the marriage annulled?' she
insisted. 'I would be the last person to object to that.'

'And how would you set about proving that the
marriage had not been consummated?' He allowed
her to digest that in silence before going on implac-
ably, 'And what about your father?'

'What about him? I'm not necessary to the business deal between you. I never was. I can't under-

132

stand——'

'*You* can't understand! My dear Emily, don't you ever think about anyone but yourself? Your father spent his whole life building up that business. How do you suppose he would feel handing it over to someone who had no connection with his family? He built it up for *you*, not for the benefit of someone he hardly knows.'

'He likes you for yourself——'

'But he thought he was giving you your heart's desire!'

'I could prove the marriage hadn't been consummated,' she threw at him, her eyes fixed on her hands in her lap. 'You don't have to go on with it. I know you think I've let you down and that you don't want the sort of woman you think I am to be your wife, so it would be much better to end it now. I'll explain it to my father and tell him it's all my fault.'

'So you are a coward too? I'm afraid you'll have to put up with the consequences of our marriage whether you want to or not. I, too, have my pride. I am well known in Greece, and I have no stomach for the gossip your departure would inspire at my expense. I may not have the virtuous wife of my expectations, but, by God, nobody else is going to know that!'

Emily shivered at the suppressed violence in his voice, genuinely afraid of him. Yet it would be a mistake to let him know that, she thought. It would be a mistake to show him any weakness at all. She raised her head and gave him back look for look.

'What are you going to do?' she asked.

'You'll see,' he said.

133

'Surely we ought to be home by now?' Emily complained, stirring in her seat. They seemed to have been driving for ever.

'Home? Is that how you think of my house?'

'I suppose I must do.'

She stirred again. The beginnings of a headache dominated her thoughts. She hardly ever had headaches, so she was apt to think it an earth-shaking event whenever she did have one.

'Don't you object to my calling it *my* house? Wouldn't you prefer me to call it ours?'

She shrugged her shoulders. 'I don't think of it as mine in any way,' she answered. If he wanted to be beastly, let him! See if she cared! Besides, it was too much trouble to think of clever answers. She yawned, hoping he would notice her new sangfroid. 'I'm quite happy to think of it as yours!' Her lips curved into a smile. 'Is your revenge to drive me around for ever getting nowhere?'

'Is that how it seems to you? I decided we would not go back to Nauplia, but Barbara had sent the yacht on to Kalamata for some reason best known to herself. I am taking you there to meet the yacht and from there we will go on to Hydra and stay in a villa I have there. We shall be alone there. Completely alone.'

Emily stretched her cramped limbs. 'I'm surprised you should want to be alone with me!'

'Are you?'

'You don't like me, and you prefer to believe Barbara sooner than you do me, although you must know she'd like to wipe the floor with your pride.'

'Barbara is my sister.'

134

'What has that got to do with it? She sounded to me as though she hates you.'

'Well, that's something you have in common.'

'I don't hate you,' she said.

He looked amused. 'Another lie?'

She bent her head. 'Must you? I was exaggerating, that's all. But Barbara's another kettle of fish entirely. She wouldn't mind seeing you bleed.' She tossed her hair back behind her shoulders. 'Why do they live with you? Why don't they have a house of their own?'

'Barbara has grown used to her creature comforts. The kind of house Giórgios could provide for her wouldn't suit her at all.'

'Poor Giórgios!' Emily sighed. 'It would be a kindness to him if you showed her the door. It isn't fair on him always being compared with someone like you.'

'He is stronger than he looks. I would never have allowed Barbara to marry him if he hadn't been.'

'*Allowed?*' Emily shot him a speaking look. 'That's exactly what I mean! Why don't you let Giórgios shine for a change? Let *him* decide where they're going to live—even how they're going to live! Why do you have to interfere all the time?'

A muscle quivered in his cheek. 'Barbara isn't given to listening much to Giórgios. I should have thought you would have approved of the woman being the dominant partner.'

'With you pulling the strings? No, thank you very much!'

'If someone didn't keep an eye on Barbara she would go to pieces altogether. If she were a man, I would have pushed her out long ago, but one can't turn a woman out of the place she considers to be her home. Giórgios pretends to himself that it's a necessary arrangement to help with Demetrios and Chrisoula——'

'Why doesn't he give her some babies of her own?'

Demis suddenly reached out a hand and patted her knee. 'Is that what I ought to do with you, Emily *mou*?'

She was taken aback. 'I don't think you ought to joke about such things,' she declared, knowing that she sounded prim and wishing with all her heart that she had one-tenth of her sister's self-possession. How Margaret would have loved such a remark! And how easily she would have turned the tables on Demis by a single witty retort that would have removed the sting as easily as Emily could make a pie-crust. 'We were talking about Barbara——'

'I prefer to talk about us. Emily, will you promise to tell the truth this once, just this once in your whole life?'

She was hurt, but she nodded her head. 'I promise.'

'Why did you suppose I married you?'

She paused, giving herself time to answer. 'You wanted my father's business.'

'The truth, Emily. You promised to tell the truth!'

'I thought the business was important to you. That *is* the truth!' She was silent for a moment. 'Was there another reason?'

He nodded his head very slowly. His eyes held hers. 'When I saw you on the train, laden down with parcels, I wanted to make love to you then. I was determined to get to know you somehow, and to see you again. My mistake was in thinking I had to marry you, but it is too late for regrets about that. You see, Emily, you are married to me and there is no reason for me not to make love to you.'

'You promised——'

'A promise I didn't think I'd have to keep. I'm not such a fool as not to know when a woman is interested in me, and you were interested all right. I thought I was giving you time to get used to the idea. Did you laugh at me for that? Well, there isn't any reason for me to wait now, is there?' He smiled fleetingly at her. It was not a nice smile and she found herself shaking inside with sheer fright.

'Please, Demis, not—not like that!'

'Why not, my Aphrodite? I deserve to get something out of the deal, surely?'

'You have my father's firm,' she whispered.

'I have you too,' he said as quietly as she. 'You won't escape me, Emily Thorne. I want you, and I mean to have you!'

She was glad of the motion of the car, glad that the fact that he was driving prevented him from touching her, giving her a chance to survey the confusion within her. If she was afraid, she would not show it, she determined. She would never show him that she was afraid!

'Emily Kaladonou,' she corrected him on a gasp. 'You may as well get it right.'

'*My* Emily,' he conceded. 'And mine you are going to be!'

She averted her eyes from his hands on the steering-wheel, picturing vividly the scene again when he had introduced her to his statue of Aphrodite and

137

had caressed the marble almost as if she had been a real woman. Of course that didn't mean anything with a Greek : they used their sense of touch as other people use their eyes, or so her father had always told her. Now, if it had been Keith she might have thought that he had been flirting with her—not that Keith would ever have been as subtle as that in his approach to any girl—but with Demis she couldn't be sure of anything.

Hermione! The other girl burst suddenly into her thoughts. How could she have forgotten about Hermione? Temper lent her courage. She lifted her chin, giving a pugnacious set to her head.

'You weren't very long in England,' she said. 'Didn't Hermione like it there?'

'I don't know if she likes England or not.'

'Perhaps you were both too busy to notice?'

His smile was less than kindly. 'You're beginning to sound like a wife—a jealous wife at that!' he remarked.

She made a noise that she hoped sounded as though she was laughing the idea to scorn. It wasn't very successful. 'Me? Jealous? What makes you think that?'

'Why else should you dislike Hermione?'

'Why does one dislike anyone? She doesn't like me either.'

'No,' he agreed, 'and she doesn't mind admitting she is jealous of you. It would have suited her very well to have been my wife. For once her father would have been proud of her, and, instead of being forced to work for him for her money, she would have been rich overnight, with two fortunes at her disposal.'

138

'Then why didn't you marry her and let her live happily ever after?' Good heavens, she thought, she was sounding sour. And he would notice too, because he always did know what she was thinking as though by some process of osmosis, transferring her thoughts from her own head to his.

'Because I would never have been the only man in her life,' he said.

She began to argue, 'You're not——'

'But I will be in the future!'

It was impossible to tell him that that hadn't been at all what she had been going to say. She cast him a swift look of dismay. Not only would he not believe her, but he would insist that she explain further, and to do that he would force admissions from her she wasn't ready to make to anyone—not even herself!

'You can't be sure of that,' she said in a voice that trembled.

'Can't I? *Can't I*, Emily?'

She bowed her head, pretending to lean forward to flick some dust from her jeans, but really to hide the fact that she could no longer conceal her emotions. She was conscious of him stopping the car and drawing her into the circle of his arms. She was unable to resist. She felt him put one hand behind her head and the other on the small of her back, moving so gently that she had hardly felt it at first, separating her blouse from her jeans.

'Have you ever been your own boss?' he asked her.

'Not yet. But I would have been.'

His fingers moved slowly up her spine. 'You'll have all my money to spend in any way you want. Isn't that enough for you?'

139

She tore herself free of him, breathless and ashamed of the weakness that had assailed her limbs at the close contact with him. 'No!' she shouted at him. 'It can never be enough! I want my own money to spend in my own way! I don't want to be told what to do for the rest of my life!'

'If you ask me,' he said, 'you don't know what you want. Grow up, little one, and admit that what you really want is me!'

She hit out blindly at the smug expression on his face, but he caught her wrist long before the blow could be delivered, and he actually had the temerity to smile at her—an amused, tolerant smile that set her pulses drumming in a confused panic of anticipation.

'Shall I prove it to you?' he asked her softly.

She made no movement at all to stop him. He held her so closely against him that there was no possible escape. She ought to have made some kind of protest, but all she felt was his lips on hers, exploring the contours of her mouth with an expertise she had never known before, drawing from her a response that shattered the last of her reserve. She wound her arms around his neck and pulled herself closer into his embrace, delighting in the hard, masculine feel of him and the strength of the arms that held her.

He kissed her cheek and the lobe of her ear, unbuttoning her blouse without her knowing that he had done so until she felt his searching fingers against the soft, swelling flesh of her breasts.

'No, Demis, please don't!'

He released her at once and pushed her back into her own seat, lighting himself a cigarette.

'Anyone would think you'd never had a man's hands on you before,' he said roughly. 'You play the young virgin very well, my dear.'

She caught her breath with difficulty, pulling the edges of her blouse together with a helpless agitation that wasn't made any better by the knowledge that he was watching her every movement and that his expression was far from kindly.

'I haven't—I mean, I've never——'

He took pity on her, doing up the buttons himself with a sardonic smile. 'No more lies, Emily. You said yourself you liked the spice of variety, remember?' He bent his head and kissed her lips, without love, as if it were an insult. 'You wouldn't escape me now, *karthiá mou*, but I grew out of making love on the back seat of a car a long time ago. I can wait for you until tonight, but I won't wait any longer, so don't waste your breath on any further excuses. Your reluctance isn't particularly convincing.'

She looked straight ahead of her, determined not to let him see how much he was hurting her.

'I wish you wouldn't use endearments you obviously don't mean,' she muttered. 'I'm no part of you —certainly not your heart!—and I don't mean anything to you.'

'You're not much of a mind-reader,' he said lazily. He picked up a lock of her hair between his fingers, pulling on it gently. 'What do I mean to you?'

She shrugged, refusing to answer. She could still feel the pressure of his arms about her, commanding her surrender, and she wondered that she didn't resent his easy mastery more.

'Never mind,' he went on, dismissing her silence

141

with what he obviously felt was the contempt it deserved. 'Fate always intended you to be mine, Emily Thorne Kaladonou.'

He stubbed out his cigarette and started up the car again.

'How much further is it to Kalamata?' she asked him.

'It's not far now.' His eyes passed over her flushed face and her still dishevelled appearance. He gestured towards her handbag. 'You'd better tidy yourself if you don't want the whole crew to start using their imaginations.' He touched her cheek with a proprietorial finger, before swinging the car out into the open road. 'There's no one more entitled to kiss you than your own husband, Emily *mou*. Blush for the other kisses you've received, not for mine! I have every right to take as many kisses from you as I want!'

It was the first time Emily had seen the yacht by daylight. The clean, sweeping lines of the prow towered above the small dinghy that took them out from the busy wharf of the harbour. She read the name *Coronis*, printed in Greek and Roman letters, and turned eagerly towards Demis.

'Did you call her after your mother?' Emily asked. 'Did she know? I mean——'

'She was already dead,' he answered shortly. 'I doubt if she'd have thought it much of an honour anyway. She would have preferred the working *caique* I had before. She wasn't easily impressed by the outward trappings of wealth.'

'It's a lovely compliment, though!' Emily exclaimed. 'I wouldn't care if it were only a tub that

142

couldn't go outside the harbour in case it sank!'

He looked at her with his old mocking smile. 'I'll name my next yacht for you,' he offered.

'Oh, yes, *please*! I'd give anything for that!'

The gleam in his eyes made her suddenly self-conscious.

'I may hold you to that,' he warned her. 'At least I shall know how to reward you, my lovely Emily. *Emily Kaladonou!*'

CHAPTER NINE

THERE were two main staterooms, both of which had direct access on to the deck. Emily, rather at a loss as to what was expected of her in the unaccustomed magnificence of her surroundings, allowed the steward to escort her into the first of the staterooms and was surprised to find it full of her own belongings.

'Where did these come from?'

'*O kyrios* commanded they should be brought on board. I have taken the liberty of unpacking the things you will need for the night only. There will be a woman who will see to your things on Hydra. I hope I have done right?'

Emily didn't like to say that no one had ever packed or unpacked for her in her life before, except possibly her mother when she had been a child.

'Thank you,' she murmured. 'It was kind of you to go to so much trouble. I've never been on a private yacht before.'

'We shall hope to serve you often in the future, *kyría*. It has been a great happiness to us to know *o kyrios* has married such a lovely woman.' The very male appreciation in his eyes startled her. An Englishman would have kept such thoughts to himself, she decided, but she must be growing more Greek by the minute, for she found it quite soothing to her ego to know that Demis' servants approved his choice and, maybe, even envied him a little.

'An English woman?'

He shrugged expressively. 'A rare flower may be found anywhere,' he answered.

'Mmm,' she agreed, 'but they don't always transplant easily.'

'Madam is joking. It's easy to see she is already Greek in her heart,' he retorted gracefully.

Then she saw Demis in the doorway. How much of the exchange had he heard? she wondered. Would he think she was being too familiar with his steward? Flirting with him even?

'Are you Greek in your heart, Emily? Yannis is a very good judge of the English mind. He fought with the British in the last war in Crete.' He sat down on the end of the gold and white double bed, completely at his ease. 'Well, *karthiá mou*?'

Emily clenched her fists. 'Most Europeans feel a little bit Greek,' she said, averting her face. 'The basis of our law—all sorts of things—came to us through the gateway of ancient Greece. In England, most of them came via Rome, but they were Greek first of all.'

'True, *karthiá mou*. But isn't there another reason why you have a Greek heart inside you?'

'None that I can think of.' Her eyelids flickered as she caught the swift glance her husband exchanged with Yannis, who openly grinned, shaking his head at her. 'I feel English through and through!'

'No, no, *kyría*,' Yannis denied, obviously still amused. He reverted to his native Greek, reminding her that English girls were either cold, or promiscuous, or both, which wasn't their fault considering the permissive lives their men allowed them to lead and that they were denied the benefit of having handsome Greek lovers for their husbands.

'How do you know so much about English women?' Emily thrust back at him, wrinkling up her nose at the unsatisfactory picture he had painted of her compatriots. 'Most of us live quite ordinary lives.'

'I heard the British soldiers talking about their wives in the war, and we have many English tourists here in Greece. The British have many virtues, you understand, they are valiant and they love justice, but they do not understand women.'

'Oh?' Emily said even more coldly.

Yannis shook his head. 'Women will always test to see if a man means what he says, and despise him if they find he does not. We Greeks understand this. In Greece, it is always the man who rules the household, but it is the woman who rules his heart. So, you see, having a Greek husband, your heart must be Greek, for it is his heart you keep within you——' He broke off, sensing Demis' faint dismissive movement. 'The Greeks also talk too much! At what hour shall I serve dinner, *kyrie*?'

Demis' eyes were on his wife's face. 'As soon as it is ready,' he answered. 'Are you hungry, Emily *mou*?'

Emily shook her head. Food had never been further from her mind. She heard the door close behind Yannis and made a play of checking that she had everything she needed for the night. He had put out a long dress for her to change into, she noticed. Made from creamy-coloured wool, it had a gold belt and some gold braiding on the bodice. It was a dress she knew she looked well in, but that wasn't how she wanted to look tonight! She wondered if she could change it and lifted the lid of her suitcase to see what else she had, deliberately avoiding her husband's eyes all the while.

'Who packed my things?' she asked, finding the silence unbearable.

'Chrisoula.' His tone was dry. 'I thought somehow that you wouldn't want Barbara going through your things.'

She looked up at him then. Had he really been so concerned for her feelings at a time when he had been undeniably angry with her?

'I like Chrisoula,' she said.

'Meaning that you don't like Barbara?'

'I didn't say that. I don't know her very well yet, so how can I say?'

'You stiffen whenever her name is mentioned. There must be some reason for that?'

There didn't seem to be anything else that would be suitable for her to wear. Chrisoula had made sure of that! There were several pairs of jeans—every pair she possessed, in fact—and tops of all kinds, both warm and cool, and several changes of underwear, but remarkably little else.

'I told her to put in your swimming things,' Demis said reflectively. 'I like to see you in the water, if it's warm enough.'

Emily didn't know how to answer that. 'One or two dresses wouldn't have gone amiss,' was what she did say. 'And I can't find any make-up at all.'

'Have a look in the dressing-table,' he advised. 'You may find something there.'

Obediently, she went and looked. In the top drawer

was a whole range of cosmetics bearing the house name of a famous Parisian firm she had heard of often, but had never been able to afford. She opened the nearest bottle of scent and tried a little on her wrist. With a small cry she recognized immediately where she had smelt it before. It had been on Hermione.

'I'd rather not use these,' she said out loud.

Demis frowned. 'What foolishness is this?' he demanded. 'Of course you will wear them!'

She held the drawer so tightly her fingers ached. 'Why should I?'

'Because I wish it.' He strode across the stateroom to her, taking the scent from her in an impatient movement. 'What is wrong with my choice? I find it very pleasant—young and innocent!'

'It isn't me,' she said stiffly.

He laughed harshly. 'You could be right! But, as they were bought with you in mind, you'll have to make the best of them—or go without!'

'How do you mean, they were bought with me in mind?' she couldn't resist asking him.

'I consulted your mother about your taste and had them sent to the yacht from a shop in Athens. It seems your mother was mistaken.'

'No, no, she wasn't.' Emily avoided the quick gleam in his eyes, feeling decidedly foolish. 'I thought they'd been chosen for somebody else.'

'Somebody else?' He sounded extremely angry.

She nodded her head. 'Did you really buy them for me?'

The glint in his eyes became more knowing. 'Do you doubt it, Emily *mou*? Whom else would I have bought them for?'

Hermione's name rose to her lips, but she swallowed it down again. 'How should I know? I don't know the names of all your women!'

He put a hand under her chin and raised her face to his. 'You're not very consistent, *agapí*. Why should you resent the women I've noticed in the past when you don't scruple to fling your boy-friends in my face? Did you expect to have a husband who had no experience of your sex at all? A Greek husband at that? You ask too much, *karthiá mou*! You're in no position to complain if I keep half a dozen mistresses, are you? But it so happens that you are the first woman I have invited on board my yacht—if it's any comfort to you!'

'Barbara——'

'Not even Barbara has been on board at the same time as myself—though as my sister she can hardly be included in the term "one of my women", can she?'

Emily hesitated. Then, 'You tell lies too!' she said suddenly.

He was sufficiently startled to release his grasp on her chin. 'Emily, I warn you——'

'You do too! You told me your sisters would give you a good reference for managing their affairs for them. That may be true of Chrisoula, but it certainly isn't true of Barbara! Is it?'

She was gratified to discover that she had disconcerted him.

'I know you've done your best for her—and I expect she knows it too, underneath. Only you did ask for me to try and strike back, you know, and I can't

149

always be expected not to throw any brick that comes to hand, even if it's clearly marked, "This one will land below the belt!" What's sauce for the goose is sauce for the gander too,' she went on, annoyed to hear a quivery note in her voice.

His arms enclosed her, drawing her up on to her feet. 'My dear girl, if you'll believe that, you'll believe anything. It may be unfair, but might is still right in the battle of the sexes. How will you prevent me from seeing other women?'

'I shan't try,' she claimed. 'It's nothing to me whom you see.'

'Is it not?' he asked. 'Including Hermione?'

'I don't wish to discuss Hermione, if you don't mind.'

He let her go, but she was equally conscious of him without his arms about her. She could feel every muscle in his body and the hardness of his flesh as much as if she were still in his embrace. She watched him pick up the bottle of scent again and hold it beneath his nostrils.

'So that was it,' he said at last. 'Jealous little cat! It isn't Hermione's usual choice, you know.' He swung round towards her. 'Next time, I'll have something especially created for you and buy the recipe so that nobody else will ever wear it. Will that suit my lady?'

'Don't be ridiculous,' she said coldly. 'You can't do things like that.'

'If one has money one can do practically anything.'

She snatched up the scent and defiantly dabbed herself with it. 'Well, you shouldn't!' she berated him. 'You shouldn't indulge anyone to that extent.

It's—it's indecent!'

His eyes held hers. His were light and seemed to look right through her. She noticed inconsequentially that his lashes provided a dark frame for them, making them seem lighter still.

'I have only one wife. Why shouldn't I indulge her if it pleases me to do so? Are you afraid I may ask more from you in return?'

She tried to disengage her eyes from his, but the power that emanated from him prevented her. 'Demis, I would have told Keith I was married. I began to tell him, but I couldn't remember my name. All I could think of was Kaladonis——'

'And your Greek isn't good enough to put my name into the possessive case?' he mocked her. 'You understood Yannis well enough when he spoke Greek to you!'

'Oh yes,' she admitted, 'I can *understand*, it's when I come to say something myself that I get all muddled up.'

'It makes no difference,' he said coldly. 'You still went with him.' He put a possessive hand on the nape of her neck, giving her a little shake. 'I do not wish to hear any more about this Keith. You will not speak of him again, Emily.' His fingers caressed her skin. 'I had better leave you to change for dinner. Can you manage on your own?'

'Of course,' she said coolly.

'Then I had better leave you to take your shower.' He favoured her with a mocking smile. 'We have every comfort on board, you will discover—everything you could possibly wish for, except the means of escaping from me!'

Emily didn't have to see herself in the long looking-glass on the back of the door to know that she was looking her very best. The folds of the long skirt accentuated the slimness of her hips, with the gold braiding giving just that touch of glamour that put the dress into that special class calculated to make it a firm favourite in any woman's wardrobe. She loved herself in it, only she hadn't wanted to wear it that night. The last thing she wanted was to accentuate her own femininity. If she could, she would have stayed in her jeans and shirt, a unisex outfit that might have made Demis forget his intentions towards herself. It hadn't worked very well so far, but in that soft, clinging dress, he could hardly forget she was a woman and his for the taking.

As she entered the saloon for the first time, she could well have been described as beautiful. Demis rose to his feet, a smile just touching the strong lines of his face.

'What will you have to drink? *Ouzo?* Or haven't you acquired a taste for our national drink yet?'

She shook her head. 'I'd prefer a soft drink, or wine. I don't go a bundle on spirits.'

He looked amused. 'No head for it?'

'No taste for it,' she answered. 'Literally. I don't like the taste of any of the usual drinks. It's very economical not to, and so I've never tried to learn to like them. I don't even like gin.'

He poured her a glass of white wine and brought it over to her. 'Your economies didn't extend to your dress,' he commented briefly. 'I like it.'

'Do you? I bought it last year. I went into the shop and fell in love with it. I couldn't not have it, though

152

it was more than I'd ever paid for a dress before. I felt guilty about it for weeks.'

'Because it ate into your savings for your restaurant?'

She nodded. 'I hadn't anything else,' she explained. 'You wouldn't understand.'

To her relief, apart from a single, piercing look, he allowed the subject to drop.

'What an incurious person you are,' he said instead. 'I thought you'd have a hundred and one questions to ask about Hydra, but you haven't mentioned it once. Aren't you interested in our destination?'

Emily stirred uncomfortably, taking a sip of wine. 'Will I like it?'

'Yes,' he said. 'I think you will. There is very little to do there, but we shall have each other——'

'I'm surprised you could spare the time from your work,' she cut him off, not at all anxious to consider what it would be like to be alone with him for more than a few minutes at a time.

'Was that meant as a nasty crack?' he smiled at her. 'I am a very successful businessman because long ago I discovered the secret of delegating things to other people. It took time, but now I have a very good team working for me and there is no reason why I can't take a few days' holiday whenever I please. There is only one thing that I can't delegate to anyone else, and that is my wife. When you know me better you will realise that I will spend days together getting a deal to go in my favour—when the deal is important to me.'

'I see,' she said. 'And as I'm part of the deal you

made with my father, you're prepared to spend some time with me?'

'Would you rather I left you to someone else?'

She took another sip of wine. 'No,' she admitted. 'I suppose not.' She stopped and began again. 'Barbara did lend me her car.'

The amusement died out of his face. 'Why must you insist on discussing an incident we would both do better to forget?'

'Because you won't believe me!'

'Very well, I shall say I believe you. Are you satisfied now?'

'No!' It was a cry from the heart. 'Because you don't! You'd rather believe Barbara!'

'And my own eyes,' he reminded her. His hand stroked her back in a soothing motion as if he were trying to calm a wild animal. It had an insidious effect on Emily's will-power. She stood up because she couldn't think straight when he was so close. She hoped she didn't look as nervous and uncertain as she felt.

'You didn't see what you thought you saw,' she told him.

'Emily, I'm trying to forget what I saw. From now on I intend to have a loving, submissive wife, one way or another. If I can't have your co-operation, I shall do without it, but I am determined to put our relationship on a proper footing before we go back to Nauplia. Is that clear enough for you?'

She bowed her head, not knowing how to answer him. Then, to her inordinate relief, Yannis came into the saloon and announced that dinner was ready and should he serve it at once?

154

Demis put himself out to be charming over the shared meal. Ignoring her dismayed face, he told her about his villa on Hydra.

'I bought it many years ago, when my parents were alive I felt the need to have somewhere on my own, where I could be by myself or with a few chosen friends.' He cast a speculative look at the angry tilt to her mouth and spread his hands in a gesture that was very Greek. 'It was somewhere to escape from the female sex, *yinéka mou*, not a love nest to escape the prying eyes of my family,' he added dryly.

'But you're taking me there!'

'Of course,' he returned with gentle menace. 'You're a part of myself—my woman, flesh of my flesh. Did you think I would leave you behind?'

Emily chose not to answer, and, after a moment's silence, he changed the subject back to the delights of Hydra.

'It's about fourteen miles long and only three miles wide in places; all of it mountainous, the highest be-ing Mount Eros which is about two thousand feet.' He saw her eyelids flicker at the mention of Eros and his eyebrows rose in a mocking look which upset her careful composure. 'Appropriately named for us,' he murmured.

'Except that we're not lovers,' she objected, not looking at him.

'Not yet,' he said.

Her stateroom seemed doubly welcome after the ordeal of dinner. Emily sank down on to the stool in front of the built-in dressing-table and stared at her-self in the glass as if she were a stranger. What annoyed her more than anything was that even alone in her room she could not be free of him. She was as conscious as ever of his strong, golden-tanned fingers and the expressive way he used his hands to make a point. She knew exactly, too, how his hair grew round his ears and at the back of his neck. She knew how it felt beneath her own fingers. She was tormented by his physical presence; the air of command he had when he kissed her; the ease with which he could compel the response which a part of her longed to deny him.

She closed her eyes against the vision of him that filled her mind's eye, and when she opened them again he was standing there just behind her shoulder, looking every inch the master that Yannis had called him. *O kyrios!* But he wasn't her master——

'I thought you'd be in bed,' he said with an ease she could only envy. He sat down behind her, looking her over in the glass with bland, masculine appreciation. He glanced down at his watch. 'I'll come back in ten minutes.' He stood up again and put out a hand, his fingers catching in her hair and dragging back her head to meet his kiss. 'Don't look so frightened, little Emily, I'm only going to love you.'

'But, Demis——'

'Why should you be more scared of me than any other man?' He kissed her lips with a contemptuous freedom that made her cry out, more in fright than in pain. He released her, frowning. 'Why do I frighten you?' he asked in more gentle tones.

Her breasts, beneath the soft wool of her dress, betrayed her agitation.

'I've never——' She took an impulsive step to

156

wards him, clutching at his shirt where it divided over his bronzed chest. 'Demis, please be kind to me!'

His arms held her close. 'Never?'

At another time she would have heard the astonishment in his voice, but she heard nothing but the thunder in her blood and felt nothing but the rising tide of need for him within her that would no longer be denied. Her dress fell to the floor round her feet and he lifted her bodily into his arms, depositing her on the down-turned bedclothes on the bed.

'Darling, it was meant from the very beginning of the world that you should be mine. Let me love you,' he murmured in Greek. But he didn't wait for an answer. He snapped out the light and slid into the bed beside her, his lips on hers.

'Your promise——' she murmured.

'Which promise?' he retorted. 'I promised I would worship your body with mine. There was no other promise which anyone in his right mind would have made to you—nor could you possibly have expected me to keep it.'

'I was only going to say it didn't matter,' she sighed. 'I thought it did——' His lips cut her off and she was glad—glad of his strength and glad of her own weakness. This was indeed what she had been born for, to be the woman of Demis Kaladonis!

'I love you,' she said.

She awoke to a sense of well-being and drowsy contentment. Demis was no longer beside her and the engines of the yacht were still so that she could hear the soft sound of the water running against the hull. She turned over lazily and saw Demis standing by the porthole looking out. A warm feeling of love, mixed up with a delighted gratitude for his remembered tenderness, welled up within her.

'Demis.' She said his name tentatively, with love.

He turned at once and smiled at her. 'Hullo, Aphrodite. My Aphrodite!' He walked back to the bed and her arms. 'You'll never get your annulment now, sweetheart. Do you mind very much?'

Her lips trembled into a smile of welcome. 'Just at the moment, I don't seem to mind at all,' she admitted. 'And you must know now that I told you the truth!'

He shrugged his shoulders. 'It matters little. I should have made love to you anyway, *karthiá mou*, if you had wanted a hundred other men before myself. You are my wife!'

She was genuinely bewildered. 'But I've never wanted any other man. I thought you knew that—that there's never been anyone else but you.'

'True.' He kissed her eyes, her cheeks, her lips, and the pulse at the base of her neck. 'I know I am the first and only man who has had your body, but am I the first to possess your heart?'

And what about his heart? she wondered. She knew she wasn't the first with him, there had been far too many others for that, but had she any place in his heart at all?

CHAPTER TEN

THE small harbour of Hydra had a distinctly Venetian look to it. It was there in the decorations around the roofs of the buildings and even more obvious in the design of the Monastery of the Dormition that dominated the waterfront.

Emily stood on the deck of the yacht and watched the busy scene on shore. A caravan of donkeys stood patiently to one side, waiting for the boat from Athens to disgorge its passengers into the souvenir shops and cafés.

'Are you coming ashore too?' she asked Yannis, who had come up on deck too. She almost hoped he would, for she was more than a little embarrassed to be alone with her husband until she had grown used to their new relationship.

'Me, *kyría*? No, *kyría*. The yacht must return to Nauplia. But you will enjoy being here, *né*? Many of our best artists have come to live here and sell their paintings in the shops. *O kyrios* knows many of them and likes to visit with them in their homes.'

'It's pretty,' Emily said slowly, 'and the colours of the houses are Greek, but the buildings look Venetian to me.'

'Of course.' Yannis shrugged expressive shoulders. 'The Venetians were everywhere. Many of the people here have Venetian blood in their veins, and not only Venetian but Armenian and, maybe, a little Turkish.

159

Hydra is famous for producing admirals and prime ministers. They are a tough people—but likeable. You like the Greeks, I am thinking, so you will like the people of Hydra.'

She hoped it would be true, but she was obsessed with nerves at being alone with Demis for several days together. She felt as though he had turned her inside out and exposed her raw nerves to the mercy of the elements. If she had been vulnerable before— and she had been where he was concerned—his lightest touch stirred her to the depths now. In other circumstances this would have brought her a profound happiness, she knew, but how could it when all the feeling was on her side and none at all on his?

'I'm going ashore,' she announced suddenly. 'Tell the *kyrios* where I've gone, will you?'

Yannis gave her a reproving look. 'You are not waiting for him?'

'No.' The single syllable sounded curt and strained and she tried to soften it with a smile, but her lips refused to curve in the appropriate way and she knew she looked every bit as uncertain as she felt. 'He won't mind,' she added.

The donkeys looked half asleep as she passed them. With heads lowered and eyes half shut, they could have been stuffed had it not been for the occasional muscle set a-quiver by a particularly persistent fly. Despite the sunshine, it was not very warm and Emily was glad of the sweater she had put on over her shirt. She would have worn a skirt, if she had had one with her, as a courtesy to the local population, who she felt were probably less accustomed to seeing females in trousers than their more sophisticated mainland brothers and sisters. This conclusion was born out by a large notice at the Monastery in both English and Greek, forbidding women to enter the church if they were wearing either trousers or shorts. To make absolutely sure the order was obeyed, the church was firmly locked anyway, but the view of the harbour through the arched entrance was so beautiful that it more than made up for any disappointment she might have felt.

Some uneven, frequently whitewashed steps led up to a balcony off which were a number of rooms, either cells for the monks, or perhaps rooms set apart for visitors in accordance with the hospitable traditions of such places in the east. Emily climbed the steps slowly with dragging feet, wondering why she was filled with an impending sense of doom. What was there for her to be afraid of?

When she turned and looked down into the court-yard below, she saw that someone had come in behind her. An instantly recognisable woman was standing in the entrance to the Monastery, leaning against the doorpost. Hermione Kaloyeropoulou was looking more lovely than ever and even more dangerous.

'Hullo there.' Emily hoped she sounded more welcoming than she felt.

'Ah!' Hermione turned slowly, her eyes two slits in her face and her smile as cold as ice. 'The blushing bride, I do declare! And no happier than the last time that we met!'

'I don't think you know me well enough to tell,' Emily retorted.

'You think not?' Hermione's throaty laugh echoed

161

round the courtyard. 'Don't be naïve, my dear. I have travelled the path you're on too often in the past not to know my way along it blindfold. Demis is as unoriginal as any other man.'

Emily slowly descended the steps. 'What do you mean by that?'

Hermione looked amused. 'This is not the first time I've been to Hydra,' she drawled.

'I imagine not,' Emily agreed. 'It isn't very far from Athens, after all. What brings you here this time?'

'Shall we say I was concerned for your welfare?'

Emily shook her head. 'I don't believe you could ever bring yourself to be concerned about me.'

'Or you about me?'

Emily managed a smile. 'I'm reasonably confident of your powers to look after yourself.'

'I cannot say the same for you!' Hermione spat out. 'You court danger with that forked tongue of yours!'

'A Thorne by name and a thorn by nature!' Emily exclaimed with deliberate flippancy.

'Did you expect to find Demis as forgiving as the other men you've known?' Hermione said. 'He will never forgive you for destroying his pride. You should have been more careful before you threw your lover in his face.'

'Keith?' Emily was shaken. 'How do you know about Keith?'

'Does it matter? Barbara told me all about it, if you must know. She was deeply shocked that Demis' newly married wife should be so perfidious. Especially after the way he had treated me!'

'Did he treat you badly?' Emily felt the words

162

dragged out of her.

'He will never allow you to dismiss your own past like that,' Hermione smiled. 'Why should you allow him to get away with it? A few Keiths don't compare with what Demis and I had together, my dear. What we may well have again once he has learned to live with his unvirtuous wife.'

'What exactly did Barbara tell you?'

'Enough.' Hermione came closer and her scent wafted on the air under Emily's nose. Emily recognised it immediately. How could she not? Wasn't she too wearing it despite her doubts of the evening before?

'There's no truth in it, you know,' she said aloud.

Hermione laughed. 'You'll have to do better than that if you mean to protect Demis' pride,' she retorted. 'What a blow it must have been to him! My God, when I think that he might just as well have married me! It's quite a joke you've played on him, isn't it? Only I don't suppose he sees it as that. Is that why you're looking so miserable? Was he beastly to you?'

Emily's expression became as haughty as she could make it. 'If you can think that of Demis, you can't know him very well,' she said.

'I expect I know him better than you ever will,' the Greek girl insisted. 'Heavens, how many times has he brought me to Hydra in the past, do you suppose? I never lived openly with him, of course, but that was because of my father, not because I didn't want to.'

'I don't believe you.'

Hermione eyed Emily quizzically. 'Don't you? You can, you know. Whose cosmetics did you suppose those were on the dressing-table?' She put her wrist close under Emily's nose. 'Didn't you recognise it as mine?'

'But Demis said——'

'He wanted to spare your feelings, I expect. There are certain conventions in these things, after all.' Hermione made a face. 'I shouldn't be talking to you like this, should I? But why should Demis have everything his own way as far as you're concerned? If you like,' she added calmly, 'you can travel back to Nauplia with me. That will give him something to think about! His wife and his mistress in the same boat, so as to speak!'

Emily couldn't bring herself to smile. 'How did you come?' she asked.

'Easily enough. I hired a boat and came. I thought that if I could find you before Demis took you to the cottage, I could spirit you away before you were silly enough to fall in love with him. Or is it too late for that?'

'I am his wife.'

'Oh yes, we all know about that!' Hermione agreed. 'But he wouldn't touch you after the incident with Keith—I know him far too well for that!—and it was all pretty airy-fairy before, wasn't it? You mustn't mind my knowing, my dear. I've been a friend of the family for years and years, and Barbara was bound to tell me her doubts about her brother's marriage sooner or later. It was you we were worried about. None of us wants to see you hurt.'

For a few moments Emily was silent, as her eyes held Hermione's. Then she said, 'It wasn't like that at all. Ours is a perfectly normal marriage.'

'Is it?'

Emily found some difficulty in continuing to meet Hermione's innocently wide eyes. She was shocked to see the momentary venom that she caught in their depths before it was overtaken with her more customary blandness.

'Why should you suppose that it wasn't?' she asked.

Hermione's face tightened. 'Barbara said—it wasn't normal before Demis went to England, was it? And Demis always sails the yacht himself when he's on board, so that nothing much could have happened last night—or did it? If it did, it was just his revenge on you—but then you already know that, don't you?'

'Have you been with Demis on his yacht often?' Emily asked quietly.

'Often and often. What did you expect?'

'That you'd probably lie to me. It hasn't worked. I'm staying with Demis, Hermione, and nothing you can say will alter that. I think you'd better go back to Barbara and tell her that.' She took a deep breath walked back through the arch into the street outside. 'Goodbye, Hermione!'

But it was one thing to put on a show for Hermione Kaloyeropoulou, quite another to convince herself. She pushed her way into the nearest café and ordered herself a drink that she didn't want, trying desperately to pull herself together before she had to face Demis.

Like a refrain in the back of her mind, his words of the night before came back to mock her, that he would have made love to her then if she had wanted a hundred other men before him. Didn't he care what

165

she thought and felt about him?

'There you are!' his voice said beside her. 'Are you trying to avoid me? Why, *agapí*? I thought I succeeded in making you very happy last night?'

'In a way,' she admitted uncertainly.

'Well, you scarcely look much of an advertisement for marital bliss this morning,' he said dryly. 'Even Yannis noticed that you looked more forlorn than radiant.'

'It's how I feel,' she muttered. She knew that he had sat down beside her, but she averted her face, wondering what he would say if she asked him to go away.

'Emily, look at me!' In spite of herself, she turned towards him, veiling her eyes from his piercing look of inquiry. 'You look rather less like Aphrodite in that sweater,' he observed. 'I'm glad I know the real you underneath.' He kissed her cheek. 'Did I tell you how beautiful you are?'

She grimaced. 'I won't be compared to that statue! Besides, I think it's a horrible thing to have in one's front hall!'

The light in his eyes was very bright. 'If I didn't know you better, I'd say you were afraid of the competition,' he said. 'Aphrodite's beauty won her the golden apple in the first known beauty competition, if you remember? Cheer up, Paris could only have agreed with me that a living beauty is better than one made of marble any day.'

'Only because it's *there*!' she told him, looking away. 'You'd have been just as happy with anyone else. I never pretended to resemble Aphrodite in the first place.'

He forced her face up to meet his glance. 'It was you who claimed to share her liking for variety in your lovers!' he reminded her grimly. 'What was I supposed to think about that?'

She shrugged her shoulders. 'I only said it to annoy you. You were doing your best to annoy me!'

His eyes narrowed. 'Was I? It sounds as though I succeeded.'

'And you lied to me too!' she went on, unable to stop herself. 'I'll never forgive you for that! If I hadn't believed you, I wouldn't—I *couldn't*——'

He was silent for a long moment. 'I think you'd better tell me what this is all about,' he said at last.

'I think you already know.' Her tone was expressionless. 'There isn't any point in staying here in Hydra, is there? I'm not the only woman you've ever brought here, and you didn't buy those things on the yacht specially for me. I should have known—I think I did know!—but I pretended to myself that I didn't. Only now I can't go on pretending. I'm sorry, but I can't!'

'I see. What do you want to do, Emily?'

She looked away from him again. 'We'd better go back to Nauplia,' she said. 'Chrisoula may need us. It isn't good for her to be left in Barbara's care.'

'Barbara is her sister,' she heard him say. 'She wouldn't do her any harm.'

Emily clenched her fists. 'You're stupid where Barbara is concerned! Oh yes, I know you say she's neurotic, but you don't see that she'd do just about anything to hurt you! You expect her to behave just like anyone else, but, where you're concerned, I don't believe she ever has!'

167

'Our quarrel was over years ago.'

'Was it? Then why did she tell you I'd taken her car without her permission, if that wasn't to hurt you through me?'

'Oh really, Emily, not that again!'

'Why not? It's the truth!'

He looked at her closely, apparently adding something up in his own mind. 'If we go back to Nauplia, you'll still be my wife. Nothing can change that now.'

She found it hard to keep her voice under control. 'But it's silly to pretend to something that isn't really there,' she objected. 'It—it was just something that happened.'

Unexpectedly he smiled. 'Just as long as you realise that it's more than liable to happen again,' he observed. 'I'll take you back to Nauplia, *yinéka mou*, but don't think you'll escape me for ever. I don't like having a miserable wife, and I won't put up with it for long, so I'd advise you to sort out whatever it is that's worrying you as quickly as you can. I'll help, if you'll let me, but in the end it will be just the same. You're my wife and sooner or later you'll take your place in my bed and be the mother of my children, no matter how unhappy the prospect makes you!' He stroked her cheek with a knowing finger, following the caress with a light kiss. 'I don't think you'd be miserable for long in my arms. Even the Aphrodites of this world have to fulfil their destiny in the end!'

'But why me?' she asked in a rush. 'There have been so many others, so why me?'

If he had said he loved her she would have turned to him then and there, but he did not. 'Because you're my wife!' he exclaimed violently. 'For better or for

168

worse, you're my wife!'

Even the yacht had lost much of its romance for
Emily. She had thought it the one place where she
could safely exclude Hermione's influence, but now it
seemed to be a living reality over which there was no
chance of them ever reaching each other.

'I hate Hermione!' she said out loud to herself as
she stood on the deck of the yacht and watched the
harbour of Nauplia coming inexorably closer. She
had not known how close Demis was to her, and she
started visibly when he put a hand on her shoulder,
his fingers biting into her flesh.

'Why?' He shook her, not particularly gently.
'What has Hermione to do with all this, Emily?'

'N-nothing,' she stammered.

'I could make you tell me, *agapí*. Have you thought
of that?'

Her eyelashes flickered. She had few doubts about
his power over her if he cared to exercise it. 'But you
won't?' she whispered.

'I might, if I thought it would make you any happier, *karthiá mou*. I'm not a patient man, so be
warned.'

'You shouldn't have lied to me,' she said on a
note of desperation. 'And it isn't only Hermione.
How many other ghosts are going to come up out of
your past?'

'Hermione need not worry you, sweetheart. It's
your imagination that allows her to haunt you—if she
does. She never did mean very much to me.'

'But you took her with you to Hydra——'

'Never!'

'Oh, Demis, are you sure?'

He looked grimmer than ever. 'I have told you so, little one, and I don't often repeat myself. I assure you that neither Hermione nor any other woman has ever gone with me to Hydra—or set foot on any yacht of mine. Satisfied?'

Her heart jumped within her. 'I wish I could believe you!' she cried out.

'But you don't. Why not, Emily?'

'Hermione herself told me——' She broke off, recognising the shape of someone she knew on the quayside. 'Patrick!' She jumped up and down in sudden excitement. 'It's my brother, Patrick! Whatever can he be doing here?'

Demis turned her roughly towards him. 'When did she tell you?'

'Does it matter?' She shrugged away from him impatiently, anxious to catch her brother's attention. 'Patrick!' she yelled across the water.

He looked up and waved, almost as though he had been expecting her. 'Hullo there! Coming ashore?'

Demis went down the gangway first, turning to help her over the awkward last step on to the concrete wharf. She put her hand in his, thinking to withdraw it immediately her feet were on solid ground, her eyes on her brother's face, but Demis threaded his fingers through hers, rubbing his thumb across her palm in an intimate gesture that robbed her of all desire to withstand him and to use Patrick as a tool for her own purpose.

'Why are you here?' she demanded.

Patrick stood still, his head on one side, watching her critically as she tried to retrieve her hand from her husband's grasp. He bent his head and touched his lips to her cheek. 'The Greek air suits you! You're looking much prettier than you ever did in London.'

She looked up at him, very conscious of Demis beside her. 'What happened? I expected to see you at Christmas, we all did. Didn't she come up to your expectations?'

Patrick gave her an easy smile. 'You never did understand the rules of the particular game. Choosing a partner for a brief whirl every now and again is quite different from choosing a partner for the rest of one's life. Most girls are only worth a dance or two before one passes on elsewhere.'

'You and Margaret both!' she said.

'But never you,' he agreed smoothly. He turned to Demis, lifting an eyebrow in amused self-mockery. 'We had almost despaired of our more prosaic sister before you whirled her into a romantic adventure that quite put our poor efforts in the shade. How did you do it? The Emily we've always known ran for cover at the first hint of involvement in an affair of the heart.'

'Oh, shut up!' Emily declared. 'I had my moments. Lots of them. I didn't see the need to talk about them, that's all!'

Patrick threw back his head and laughed. 'I've known you far too long to believe that story! And I always thought you such a truthful girl!'

Emily cast a slanting glance at Demis and was discomfited to see him exchange a look of complete understanding with her brother.

'You have known her—and not known her,' Demis said, shaking hands with their uninvited guest. 'Emily

171

is by far the most romantic of the Thornes, and if you found her truthful before it can only have been because she had nothing to fib about. She bends the truth with an ease that would astonish the most accomplished liar——'

'I do not!' Emily could see nothing funny about her indignation, but both the men began to laugh. 'Truly, I don't!'

Demis squeezed her fingers between his. 'Cheer up, little one, I'm sure Aphrodite also only told the truth when it suited her. It is something else you share with that goddess. What a pity it is we can't ask Patrick's opinion.'

'Demis——'

Patrick looked from one to the other of them. 'A certain similarity of form, perhaps?' he queried. 'Mind you, I might not have noticed it if Chrisoula hadn't pointed it out to me.'

'Chrisoula! Patrick, how could you? She's only sixteen!'

'My dear Emily, she's years older than you'll ever be,' her brother retorted, still smiling.

She felt Demis squeeze her hand. 'Chrisoula is mature beyond her years,' he agreed, 'but it is true she is only sixteen. She will be in my care for quite a few years yet.'

'Of course,' Patrick answered calmly. 'You don't have to worry, my friend, she herself has already pointed that out to me.'

Demis released Emily and left the brother and sister alone together, walking away from them across the wharf to where Patrick had parked Barbara's car beside the café.

Emily watched Chrisoula jump out of the car and greet Demis with her usual exuberant affection.

'Patrick, why did you come?'

'Oh, I don't know,' he answered. 'I think I wanted to see for myself that you were all right. Everybody said you were, but your new husband had pretty well devastated any confidence we might have had in ourselves as a family. I was worried about you.'

'But did you know Demis?' she demanded.

Patrick shrugged. 'Not well. I think if I'd been a girl I would have found marriage to him rather a dismaying prospect, and you've always been such a defenceless little thing. I thought I'd come along and see for myself. But he seems different today—much more human, if you know what I mean?'

But Emily was scarcely listening. 'Oh, Patrick, thank you! I couldn't be more pleased to see you——'

'Oh, quite,' he cut her off. 'We'll talk about it later, shall we?' He made an appreciative sound with his lips. 'That sister-in-law of yours bids fair to be a little beauty, and she's a darling with it! Now that I'm here, you'll have your work cut out to get rid of me!'

Emily raised her eyebrows. 'Don't ever change!' she told him. 'I think I'd die of shock if you didn't find some female you could approve of in a monastery. But be careful of Chrisoula, brother of mine, she's in my care too.'

They walked over to the car together, Emily returning Chrisoula's hug with one of her own.

'We didn't expect you back so soon,' the young girl told her. 'And don't scold me for coming here alone with Patrick, because there was nothing else to be done. Barbara had one of her headaches. It's beautiful that you've come back, because Patrick has never been to Nauplia before and I want to show him everything. If Demis is still on holiday, we could all go and look at most places together, couldn't we? Oh, please say we can!'

Emily didn't know how to answer that and turned a look of inquiry on her husband. 'Are you still on holiday?' she asked him.

'I am.' He smiled at his young sister. 'Where do you want to go first?'

Chrisoula looked confused. 'I don't know,' she admitted. 'Emily shall choose. May we go tomorrow?'

Demis's eyes fell on Emily's face. 'Well, *agapi*?'

Her reply came without hesitation. 'May we go to Epidaurus? Please, Demis?'

Her husband's face hardened. 'Haven't you been there before?'

'No,' she said. 'I wouldn't go there without you, you know that. How could I, when your mother was called Coronis, and—and everything else?'

'Then to Epidaurus we'll go!' he declared in quite different tones. And there was no mistaking the special ring in his voice.

'You don't mind?' she pressed him.

'Mind, *korítsi*? No, I don't mind. Epidaurus will be the perfect setting for me to reveal myself as hero, and more than hero, a god to be obeyed by a mortal woman such as yourself. And you know something? I think you'll be as relieved as I shall be to meet your destiny finally face to face!'

174

CHAPTER ELEVEN

PATRICK proved unusually co-operative about moving the statue of Aphrodite from the hall to a secluded part of the garden.

'It's a bit obvious standing around in the entrance, isn't it?' he said to Demis.

'Especially as Emily blushes whenever she looks at it,' Demis replied. Emily was very conscious of his eyes upon her. 'When she's quite grown up I'll take her to look at the original in Athens.'

She looked up at him with deliberation. 'And what do I have to do to prove I am grown up?'

Demis gave her his whole attention, ignoring Patrick altogether. 'Have you grown up enough to kiss me of your own accord?'

'I might have,' she said slowly.

His golden skin blurred before her eyes as she hastily lowered her lashes. Her heart pounded against her ribs as she reached up and put her lips against his. The kiss began with a touch as soft as the wings of a butterfly, but his lips were as hard and demanding as hers were tentative. She emerged from his embrace breathless and dishevelled and very conscious of her brother's interested eyes watching the scene.

'Now tell me I'm still a child!' she invited.

He smiled. 'When you can kiss me like that without any help from me, then you'll be completely grown up!'

'As grown up as Hermione?' she hit out before she could stop herself.

His face hardened. 'Hermione has nothing to do with you.' He turned on his heel. 'I'll leave the two of you to dispose of Aphrodite as you think fit.' And he was gone before Emily could think of anything to delay him. She shrugged her shoulders, principally for Patrick's benefit. Then, she looked the goddess straight in the eyes and noticed for the first time the quizzical tolerance in her expression as she lifted her sandal preparatory to delivering a telling blow across the goat-man's cheek. It was almost as if she were amused by the emotional turmoil that ran like a hurricane through Emily's bloodstream every time Demis came near her.

'Hermione?' Patrick asked her.

'Who else? What chance have I against a woman like that?'

'Not having met the lady I really couldn't say,' her brother answered. 'But I shouldn't have said you had much to worry about. Mother and Margaret were green with envy that this beautiful Greek should have come along and swept you off your feet, and, even allowing for their powers of exaggeration, something must have made you cast yourself off into the unknown. Knowing your prejudice against romantic gestures, I presumed it was the full-blown love bit. I haven't seen anything here yet to make me change my mind. So, was I wrong?'

'Not entirely.'

'You are in love with him, then?'

'Oh yes!' she said in a carefully controlled voice, 'but he still hankers after Hermione, you see.'

'He married you.'

'Yes, but we didn't know each other—not then. I met him on the train home for Christmas. He gave me his seat. And then Mother said he had rung up at home and asked to speak to me, but that was before we had set eyes on each other, so he couldn't have done, could he?'

'Why not? He certainly rang me several times——'

'You mean you already knew him? Nobody told me that!'

'Well, I didn't know him exactly. I knew of him, though. He and Father had put through one or two deals together through the firm. I don't think Father had actually met him either, but he liked doing business with him.'

'But you don't have anything to do with Father's business,' Emily said. 'Why should he get in touch with you?'

'He was concerned about Father.'

'I don't understand——'

'I didn't either. I told him I had no interest in the firm, that none of us had—including you—I may have talked about you a bit. He was pretty tight-lipped about it all. Said perhaps I should show more interest in the future, and rang off. I didn't think anything more about it at the time. I asked Margaret if she had heard of a Greek customer of Father's and she spun me a whole yarn about receiving so many calls from strange men that if she heard a man's voice she didn't know nowadays she put the receiver down as soon as he spoke.'

How like Margaret that was!

'But what did he want?' Emily pressed.

'That was the one thing none of us knew. Next thing I heard, he had married you and taken you back to Greece with him. But he was back in England a few days later——'

'I know,' Emily said, and added, 'With Hermione!'

'Rubbish. He didn't have anyone with him when I saw him. He had the lot of us there—Mother included—and told us exactly what he thought of us. It was pretty humiliating, because it had never occurred to any of us that Father was having a sticky time of it. Peter summoned up enough spirit to ask him what it had to do with him, and he told us he was taking over the business in return for paying Father a whacking great pension for the rest of his life——'

'That's why he married me, to get his hands on the business. He insisted Father handed it over to him as my dowry. They arranged it between them.'

'Emily, you've got to be joking! We had the full bit at that memorable meeting about you being the only one of us worth her salt. He'd left you behind in Greece only so that you wouldn't hear what he thought about the rest of us. We may have battened on Father all our lives, but we weren't going to batten on him! Come to think of it, he excepted Mother from that, and Margaret up to a point because as a female dependent he didn't expect her to stand on her own feet, but to be guided by her husband. Poor Peter's face was a study! Between us, we bore the brunt of the dressing-down, which I have to admit I think we deserved.'

Emily felt moved to protest against her will. 'He had no right——'

'Why not? You made him part of the family.'

'He had the business in payment for me.'

'What a bargain! I'm trying to tell you, Emily love, that since Father's illness the business is practically bankrupt—and none of us had been interested enough to see the signs of the coming crash. Father had always managed, and it didn't occur to one of us to wonder how he was going on managing from his bed.'

Emily gave him a quick look. 'But if the firm was bankrupt, why should Demis want it?'

Patrick shrugged. 'Don't ask me! When he rang me up he was busy washing his hands of the lot of us. He only told me to look into Father's affairs out of a sense of duty towards an elderly, sick man. What a dowry! All you brought him was a lot of bills and the obligation to pick up the tab on Father's pension for the rest of his and Mother's life!'

'But why didn't he tell me? Didn't I have a right to know?'

Patrick chewed his lower lip thoughtfully. 'If you ask me,' he said finally, 'he didn't want you to know anything about it. He probably had some idea that he wanted you to love him for himself and not for what he could give you——'

'But I do!'

'But have you told him that? It seems to me that he's under the impression you're neither his, nor not his, at the moment, if you see what I mean. What reason did you give him for marrying him?'

'It was rather complicated,' she said delicately. 'Mother had told Father that this Greek had rung up inquiring for me and—and that he was very much in love with me. No, I think it was that I had fallen in love with him! You know what Mother is! And

179

Father was so excited about it all that I hadn't the heart to tell him the truth. I couldn't see that it would do any harm to pretend that I had met someone I was interested in—Father looked so ill and said that I would have done anything to make him feel better. Well, anyway, he asked me what the man's name was and I told him it was Demis Kaladonis. I thought I'd invented the name, but I hadn't. I must have seen it on his briefcase when he gave me his seat on the train. Then the next thing I knew he was at the front door and nothing I said would make him go away! He went upstairs and talked to Father for a while. And then he took me out to lunch and told me he and Father had agreed that I should marry him right away.'

Patrick's astonishment now was as great as her own, when she looked back at her own meek acceptance of the fate which had been held out to her.

'You mean you went along with that?' Patrick was still amazed.

'What else could I do? I had told Father I was in love with him. Then he said if things didn't work out he'd arrange to get the marriage annulled and would set me up in a restaurant of my own. But that wouldn't have been enough in itself. I think—I think I wanted to marry him!'

Patrick's jaw sagged as he gazed at her. 'No wonder he thinks you're the most romantic of us all! My God, you really do things properly, don't you? Even Margaret looks before she leaps into space, whereas you—you take off like that eagle that tried to fly up into the sun!'

'I couldn't help myself.' She spoke almost as though she was in a trance. 'But oh, Patrick, wouldn't it be marvellous if I made it to the sun, after all?'

'And be burned to a crisp?'

'Not with my sun! Not with Demis!'

A couple of gardeners approached, and Patrick said hurriedly, 'Spare me the star-spangled details! But you're a fool if you don't tell him how you feel. He's bound to know sooner or later.'

'And what about Hermione?' Emily's tone was as matter-of-fact as she could make it.

'Oh, hang Hermione!' her brother retorted, and bent to help the gardeners with their removal of the statue.

Epidaurus was deserted.

A wintry sunshine filtered through the pine trees whose scent lay heavy on the air. It was every bit as beautiful as Emily had expected it to be, and yet it was not in the least pretty. The famous theatre was particularly fine, and only partly restored for the benefit of the summer crowds who flocked there to see the classic plays in their original setting. It was one of the few theatres of ancient Greece that had not been altered to suit the changing tastes of their later Roman masters. It meant that one could sit any-where on the step-like seats and look out across the magnificent view beyond. And it was not just modern man who had marvelled at this particular theatre. Pausanius, a doctor of the first century after Christ, had said of it: '... in size the theatre of Megalopolis in Arcadia is superior, but for harmony and beauty, what architect could vie with Polyclitos? For it was Polyclitos who made this theatre and the round build-ing also.'

Emily had not yet visited the round building, or

181

thólos, where it was thought the sacred snakes had been housed, the same snakes that had effected many of the cures at this most famous Asklepeion of them all. Like some Lourdes of a pre-Christian era, it was here that the sick had come in their hundreds to bathe in the sacred waters and to be cured in their dreams while they slept. The cult of Asklepios had spread far and wide, and many other centres of healing had come into being, but it was here that the god had first earned his famous name among men, and it was here that modern man still came to pay him honour, as they do also by using his serpent as the symbol of the medical man to this very day.

Emily climbed to the very top of the theatre, leaving her husband far down below her. She could not see Patrick and Chrisoula at all, and she half suspected that they had deliberately taken off by themselves. From where she was seated she could see over the tops of the pine trees to the tawny hills beyond. It was possible to glimpse the complex of ruined buildings that had once made up the ancient hospital, with temples dedicated to Artemis, to the Egyptian Apollo and Asklepios, to Aphrodite, to Themis, to Asklepios himself, this time on his own, as well as the great altar that was also dedicated to him. There had been baths and a library, and dormitories where the sick had lain waiting their turn for a possible cure, a hotel, and even a gymnasium.

The followers of Asklepios had maintained that a radical healing could only take place when the mind itself was cured. If the disease of the mind lingered on, it could at any time call forth other disharmonies of the body. Was her sense of Hermione's hold over Demis just a figment of her imagination? Would

Asklepios come to *her* aid if she addressed him with the proper piety the ancient Greeks had considered so important?

Looking down, she could see her husband in the centre of the stage, his head thrown back as he watched her every moment. He looked incredibly small and distant. And then he began to speak, and she was astonished to discover that she could hear his every word as clearly as if he had been sitting next to her. Was it possible that he was talking to her? The way he spoke it, it sounded like a love poem, and a fountain of delight grew inside her as she listened to him.

> *Much have I travelled in the realms of gold,*
> *And many goodly states and kingdoms seen;*
> *Round many western islands have I been*
> *Which bards in fealty to Apollo hold—'*

She had shut her eyes to listen the better to his rich, golden tones, but now opened them wide to see why he had stopped. It was impossible not to recognise the two figures who had joined him on the stage below. One of them was Keith, scuffing his feet like an ill-at-ease schoolboy; the other was Hermione— a well-groomed, confident Hermione.

'Is this your latest conquest?' she heard Demis ask her.

'Certainly not. I don't play around with children— as you should know, Demis *mou*.'

'Not yours, now or ever!' Emily heard him reply.

'No? Well, Keith is your little wife's conquest. He was getting lonely, he had seen so little of her in the last few days. I told him she was to be found on Hydra, and here we were discussing ways and means for him to join her. What happened? Did you leave her there on her own?'

Emily saw her husband tauten almost imperceptibly. 'How did you know she was on Hydra?'

Hermione laughed her sexy, throaty laugh. 'I saw her there. Didn't she tell you? If you were kind—and you are sometimes, aren't you, my sweet?—you'd let her go home to the nursery and indulge yourself with someone who understands the needs of a real man!'

'Is that what you told her, Hermione?'

'Of course not. I merely implied that while she was your wife—if wife you can call it—I hadn't finished with you yet, not by a long way, and she was wise enough to listen to me. Forget her, *agapón*! I am much more of a woman than she'll ever be!'

Demis was too far away for Emily to see his expression, but the tone of his voice was forbidding.

'I have tasted everything you have to offer, Hermione Kalayeropoulou, and the offering was stale then. For five years I have tolerated your insinuations and your hopes that I might return to your bed only because I like and respect your father. My wife has more to satisfy me in her little finger than you have in your whole body.' He sounded suddenly amused, and Emily could imagine exactly what was in his mind as he said, 'She shares the secrets of Aphrodite, the goddess of love herself, and is more than woman enough for me! You're more of a fool than I think you are if you don't realise the truth of that for yourself.'

'But Barbara said——'

'Ah yes, Barbara! Not even Emily is naïve enough

to believe anything Barbara could say about me. Her mistake was in listening to you. It's a mistake I shall enjoy putting right at the very earliest opportunity. I'm in love with my wife, and I have reason to believe that she's in love with me,' he added reflectively. 'Goodbye, Hermione.'

'Goodbye? You think you can simply bid me goodbye after all the insults you have hurled at my head? Have I nothing to say——'

'You never had,' Emily heard him say simply. 'Goodbye, Hermione.'

Emily saw Keith pull Hermione away from the stage as the other girl shouted abuse. It came to Emily that it was not Demis' love that Hermione had wanted—it never had been—it was his money.

Demis turned his back on her, looking upwards to where Emily was sitting. 'As I was saying,' he went on calmly. He hesitated for an instant. 'You are listening, aren't you, Emily?'

She nodded her head so slightly that she thought he hadn't seen her consent, but it seemed he had, for he went on as if nothing had happened,

'Oft of one wide expanse had I been told
That deep-browed Homer ruled as his demesne;
Yet did I never breathe its purse serene
Till I heard Chapman speak out loud and bold:
Then felt I like some watcher of the skies
When a new planet swims into his ken;
Or like stout Cortez, when with eagle eyes
He stared at the Pacific—and all his men
Looked at each other with a wild surmise—
Silent, upon a peak in Darien.

185

Now do you understand, Emily?'

She almost fell a dozen times as she raced down the uneven steps into his arms. He gathered her close and, looking up, she saw his eyes were very kind.

'Make me your golden realm, Demis!' she burst out. 'That's all I ever wanted, right from the beginning!'

'I intend to, my love. You were my expanse from the moment I set eyes on you on that train. Destiny spoke and there could never be another woman for me. Are you ready for me to enter my kingdom at last, my Aphrodite?'

'Yes, please,' she said.

Sitting close beside her husband in the best marble seats that the theatre had to offer, Emily could almost believe that they were the joint rulers of the ancient world about them.

'You didn't take Hermione to England with you, did you?' she said aloud. 'But I thought you did.'

His mouth tightened. 'I shall never forgive her for deliberately setting out to hurt you! But then, I'm ashamed to say, I thought a little jealousy would do you no harm, that it could only make you more aware of me and what I hoped to mean to you.'

'You took her to Athens?'

He shook his head, his eyes full of affectionate laughter. 'I did not. Hermione had said she had come to visit Barbara, and finding Barbara still away she went on to stay with friends of hers at Patras. Satisfied?'

186

'Almost. It's rather lowering to feel the way I felt about Hermione, though.'

She hesitated, then wound her arms round his neck, freely offering him her lips. 'S'agapó pára polí,' she whispered. 'I love you very much.' She kissed him with every bit of conviction at her command. 'May we go back to Hydra one day?' she asked him. 'Just the two of us, as you wanted it before, only this time'—there was a hint of mischief in her tone— 'without Hermione.'

'My darling Aphrodite,' he said against her lips. 'Does any man refuse an invitation to heaven with the goddess of his dreams?'

The villa in Hydra was primitive by any standards, but to Emily it was a paradise that had been brought alive for her by her husband. When it was warm enough, which wasn't as often as either of them would have liked, he took her swimming and called her Aphrodite until she retaliated by refusing to answer to the name.

'I'm not at all like her!' she declared. 'How can you say I am?'

His eyes moved over her possessively. 'You are as beautiful as she. I was sure of it as soon as I saw you, and now that I have seen you as she is, I know it's so.' He smiled at her flushed face. 'How can you still be shy of me? Don't you like it when I find pleasure in your shape?'

She made a face at him. 'I suppose so.'

She didn't add that she, too, found pleasure in looking at him, but she could well have done so. She revelled in the golden shine to his skin, her own particular realm of gold and one that she had feared might never be hers.

He pulled her close against him, slipping his hands up beneath her sweater. 'Tell me again that you love me,' he commanded.

'I love you,' she responded obediently.

He kissed her slowly, savouring the salt on her lips. She pressed herself closer to him, burying her fingers in his curling hair.

'I never thought to be so happy as I have been here with you. Will it always be like this?' she whispered.

His kisses grew more demanding until she was weak with longing for him. 'This can only be the beginning for both of us,' he murmured.

She stirred in his arms. 'Please go on loving me,' she whispered.

He leaned up on his elbow, his eyes alight with the glow of the setting sun. The expression on his face told her more than words could ever have done as he got to his feet and pulled her up beside him. Slowly, he kissed her again.

'It's time for us to go inside, Emily *mou*,' he said at last. 'Shall I light the lamps or will you?'

She smiled, knowing exactly how it would end. 'Neither of us,' she sighed. 'Oh, Demis, I do love you so much!'

'Then come inside and prove it to me!' he suggested.

Other titles by Elizabeth Hunter available in the Mills & Boon Romance series

For details of how to obtain the titles listed above, please
turn to page 191.

Forthcoming Paperbacks

ISLE AT THE RAINBOW'S END *by Anne Hampson*
For Kara there could be no romance on the island of Bali –
or could there?

THIS MAN HER ENEMY *by Lilian Peake*
Doranne hated Keiran Richmond, but he still had power
over her . . .

SWEET PROMISE *by Janet Dailey*
Rafael Torres could wreck Erica's life – how was she to stop
him?

A SENSE OF WORDS *by Madeline Charlton*
Dieter disapproved of Judith – but she'd soon show him he
was wrong!

THE MARQUIS TAKES A WIFE *by Rachel Lindsay*
A visit to Africa involved Beth with the Marquis of Powys,
but she was only his grandmother's companion . . .

BLUE SKIES, DARK WATERS *by Margaret Pargeter*
Jan was suspicious of Earl Elton, but then he seemed to
suspect *her* motives. And when she fell in love with him . . .

THE MAN ON HALF-MOON *by Margaret Way*
Katharine's missing brother was her only problem, until she
met Curt Dangerfield!

THE BLACK KNIGHT *by Flora Kidd*
Sandy thought that Lymond Caldwell was like a knight of
olden days – but could he save her from falling in love?

THE UNWILLING BRIDEGROOM *by Roberta Leigh*
Melisande blackmailed André into marrying her – and only
then fell in love with him . . .

TULIPS FOR AUGUSTA *by Betty Neels*
Until she found out how Susan fitted into Constantijn's
scheme of things, how could Augusta take him seriously?

35p net each

Available February 1977

Your Mills & Boon Selection!

All priced at 25p. Please tick your selection and use the handy
order form overleaf.